A SACRED BEGINNING

*Nurturing Your Body, Mind, and Soul
during Baby's First Forty Days*

SARAH BRANGWYNNE & SASHA ROSE OXNARD

ANCIENT FAITH PUBLISHING ☦ CHESTERTON, INDIANA

A Sacred Beginning: Nurturing Your Body, Mind, and Soul during Baby's
First Forty Days
Copyright ©2021 Sarah Brangwynne and Sasha Rose Oxnard

Published by:
    Ancient Faith Publishing
    A Division of Ancient Faith Ministries
    P.O. Box 748
    Chesterton, IN 46304

ISBN: 978-1-944967-64-2

Library of Congress Control Number: 2021937609

Printed in the United States of America

DEDICATION

SARAH

To Leana, Audrey, and Edith, my most beloved teachers: you are my greatest blessings. To Katherine, my mother, who taught me about God and unconditional love. I am forever grateful you are my mom. And to my husband, for loving me as I am and holding my hand through each adventure.

SASHA

To my mother, Ariadne—my best friend, my spiritual rock, an amazing grandmother, and the one who taught me never to abandon God and assured me He would never abandon me. To my husband in thanks for his big heart and deep wisdom—both spiritual and worldly. And to my four most precious gifts—Tristan, Natalia, Andrei, and Niko—who have been my biggest teachers and greatest joys, and who continue to inspire and encourage me to love, and love more, and love more.

Contents

Preface

SARAH

Deep in the night, I was unable to fall back asleep after feeding my three-month-old baby. My mind was full of reflections about being a mother. Although daily life was a bit overwhelming now that I was a mother of three, I relished my growing family. Preparing well for my third time postpartum, after failing to heed good advice to rest and let others help after my first two daughters were born, eased the transition and allowed me to recover in peace.

Being back in early motherhood after five years, I couldn't believe how much easier it all was, in large part due to the experience and confidence gained from having my previous babies. Becoming a mother was always a dream of mine, but when I first became a mother I was in shock over how intense caring for a baby was. Becoming immersed in the world of parents and children, I quickly learned that I wasn't the only one who felt this way. Why had no one told me? Where was the guide on how to really do this—not just information on how much my baby needed to eat and sleep? A spark of excitement propelled me out of bed to journal about writing a book to share my insights and ideas so they might help other new moms in the early days of motherhood. After getting some thoughts down on paper, I was finally able to fall into a deep sleep.

SASHA

I struggled tremendously with being away from church after the births of my first two children, and during my third pregnancy I found myself dwelling on the upcoming isolation a lot. Deep down my biggest fear was that I would grow distant from my church family and spiritually dull—both things I felt I had let happen during my first two postpartum forty-day periods at home. I found myself wishing I had some kind of a spiritual companion book for my forty days and decided to try to put together a compilation of daily spiritual readings, reflections, and lives of the saints that I could read and meditate on while away from church. I ordered a bunch of books, including *Marriage as a Path to Holiness, Children in the Church*, and *Raising Them Right*, and planned to put together some spiritual reading that would give me structured reflections for my forty days ahead.

Sadly, the books collected dust, for the most part, as I busied myself with other things. When, a month before I was due, Sarah had her baby, I found myself wishing I had put the readings together for her. We chatted about what a need there was for a book like this and how we should write one together. Finally, several weeks after my son was born, I found myself lying with a sleeping child on my chest and noticed my neglected pile of spiritual books. In this quiet moment I picked up one of the titles and started reading. The words felt like a crucial reminder of what is truly needful. When Sarah called a few days later to check in, I was excited to share.

SARAH

Soon after my midnight brainstorm I called Sasha to see how she was doing a few weeks postpartum with her third child. She shared she was reading some helpful spiritual books.

SASHA: It makes me excited to write our book for new mothers.

SARAH: Our book? Sash, that is so crazy—I just wrote in my journal the idea to write a book for mothers during the first forty days!

SASHA: What? We talked about this!

SARAH: We did? When?

SASHA: A couple of months ago. Right after you gave birth. You don't remember?

SARAH: I don't think so. *(Scanning my memory, I had a vague sense of recognition.)*

SASHA: We did. You were in your forty days and we talked about it.

SARAH: Hmm, maybe, but it is so fuzzy. I wasn't sleeping much then.

Sleep was still elusive, but I was able to remember a glimmer of the conversation. We laughed about the effects of sleeplessness. We laughed again when writing this preface, as Sasha had forgotten about starting to read her collection of spiritual resources during her early postpartum days.

This is the story of how our book was born. We tell it to share our book's origins and because early motherhood is hard. It helps to be able to look back with a smile.

Introduction

She knew exactly as much as every newborn mother who had come before her knew—everything, and nothing. All at once. In that order. It was the perfect balance.

—HANNAH LAMPREY[1]

The birth of a child is one of the most momentous and joy-filled experiences in a woman's life. Many of us are surprised to discover that this joy is often tempered by the reality and demands of new motherhood. With several years of childrearing and multiple births between us, we've discovered that having been through it before made the transition a bit easier each time we brought a new child home. Knowing this, the one thing we always wish we could give new mothers is experience. Of course, true experience is gained from being in the trenches of the constant feedings, sleeplessness, and fatigue that constitute life with a new baby. During this singular time, having guidance on how to survive and thrive in our soul, body, and mind, as well as the knowledge we are not alone, is invaluable.

---

1   www.fourthtrimestercollective.com, a resource site for moms.

This book offers that guidance to fellow women from a uniquely Christian perspective. As lifelong friends who have gone through the ups and downs of motherhood together, we longed for spiritually based help during the early days. We wrote this as the book we wish someone had given us when we embarked on the journey of motherhood so that we could read and reread it each time we bring a new child home. Now we have something to hand mothers to give them the resources to build the spiritual stamina needed to raise a child of God in our modern world.

This Book Is for You

You may be a first-time mom not quite sure how your life is about to change, or perhaps you've had a child already and realize you'd like a bit more support this time. Maybe you bought this book because you're curious what spiritual life has to do with motherhood, or you need some help remembering. Maybe you crave spiritual reflection for this unique time with its unique challenges. Our hope is to give you practical, emotional, and spiritual support as you begin this journey with your new baby.

While both of us were raised in the ancient traditions of the Eastern Orthodox church, this book is written for all Christians and, truly, for anyone seeking to understand the first days with a new child in a spiritual way. Whether you are new to Christianity or Orthodoxy, were raised in the Faith but have lost touch, or are simply curious, we hope this guide will open the door to the depth of love and wealth of guidance that embracing God through the mysteries of the Faith can bring to this time.

Motherhood as a Journey

As Christians, the purpose of our lives is to live in a way that will bring us close to God, and ultimately to find eternal salvation in His all-merciful and loving presence. Our book is foremost a look at motherhood as a spiritual journey on the path to salvation. In becoming mothers, we grow our capacity for love and compassion, and yet we also experience loss, struggle, and sacrifice. It is this dual nature of motherhood that allows for such depth of joy as well as sorrow in the same moment. This complexity can be a great teacher if we open ourselves to the gift God has given us to help us work out our salvation.

The Spiritual Scaffolding for This Book

In looking to create a solid spiritual foundation for our book, we chose to use the rungs of the ladder of St. John Climacus's influential work, *The Ladder of Divine Ascent,* as our spiritual guide. While we wrote our book for mothers following the birth or adoption of a child, the spiritual learning during this period will stay with us for a lifetime. We wanted to offer something rooted in deep truths and understanding of the human heart, rather than relying solely on our own understanding and perspectives. Saint John's *Ladder,* written in the seventh century, has come down to us through centuries of prayer and wisdom with a deep understanding of God and the Christian life. The ladder itself is composed of thirty rungs, each a passion or virtue, on which St. John offers his insight, reflections, examples, and guidance. While St. John wrote for monastics, whose discipline is far above the spiritual rigor most of us will pursue, it is a useful guide for all Christians due to the depth of wisdom it contains.

Saint John's original text is challenging, and many laypeople shy away from reading it. Archimandrite Vassilios Papavassiliou wrote an invaluable book entitled *Thirty Steps to Heaven: A Guide to the Ladder of Divine Ascent for All Walks of Life* to make St. John's teachings accessible for those of us living in the world. In reading this work in tandem with St. John's original, we were struck by how the ladder offers a parallel between the attainment of holiness as a monastic and the spiritual growth we can strive for as mothers. A monastic takes a vow to enter a new life lived for God; as mothers, we make a vow to enter a new life dedicated to caring for the new soul entrusted to us.

As Christians, we are called to live our lives in Christ: to emulate Him and follow His teachings as best we are able. This is not easy. To love without ceasing, to give of ourselves, to turn the other cheek, to be humble—these actions take courage and strength. In motherhood there is much delight, deep love, and profound joy. There is also pain, struggle, and confusion as we navigate the depth of our souls that motherhood demands. Whether or not we are always aware of it, we live in a state of spiritual warfare, and the stakes are high. Let us be steadfast and sure of our goal from the beginning of our children's lives.

We want to be clear that we do not view these early days of motherhood as a time to task ourselves with spiritual growth. The nature of having a child will do this for us. We offer this book to support mothers in this naturally unfolding process, a process we believe was given by God to help us in our journey toward Him. In the Bible, St. Paul writes that having children is a way for women to be saved: "Nevertheless she will be saved in childbearing if they continue in faith, love, and holiness, with self-control" (1 Tim. 2:15). We understand this to mean that the bearing of children (which includes the raising of children and bearing them through

life), done faithfully in the Lord with love and obedience, can help
lead to our salvation.

⌣

*I think just giving myself fully to the care of a newborn con-
nects me to God, and I try to not have further expectations of
myself.*

— JULIANA, ORTHODOX MOTHER

⌣

We find our salvation as we negotiate the constant struggle
between self and other, selfishness and selflessness. Through
motherhood's joys, challenges, and trials we are tested in our
virtues, our passions become known, and our souls are laid bare.
Much like what happens to metal in the smelting fire, our impu-
rities are brought to the surface, and we have the opportunity to
let them be burned up in God's purifying love as we repent and
change our heart and actions. With this view, we see motherhood
as a form of climbing the ladder toward God and the first forty
days as a sacred time to allow the new family to form a bond and
renew the spiritual foundation that will guide them in the days,
and years, that follow.

It is important to recognize that ascending the ladder is not
a linear process. We do well to see the ladder as a guide whose
rungs are stepping stones; some we may skip to revisit later, some
we may find ourselves coming back to (again and again) until one
day perhaps we more fully internalize the lesson. With each new
church year, each new fast, each great feast, we battle toward connection with God; we fall down, get back up, and keep trying.

We also know that this process will take a lifetime for most
of us, so while we visit each rung over the course of forty days,

we do not hope to ascend to the top of the ladder in this time. Rather, we hope to plant the seeds for growth, to open our hearts and eyes to the pitfalls that may trouble us on our path and to the virtues that will help us to overcome them. Having a new baby, whether our first or tenth, is hard. This concept of ascending the ladder is in no way suggested as a sort of spiritual to-do list, but rather as an offer to use this time, as we are called to use all our time on earth, as a means of coming closer to God.

How to Read This Book

The Orthodox Faith is holistic and guides all aspects of our lives, giving us concrete guidance on how to bring our bodies, minds, and souls ever closer to God. With this in mind, we offer reflections on the struggles and triumphs of motherhood as well as wisdom from our holy elders, lessons learned from the lives of the saints, prayers, exercises, practical guidance, and voices from other mothers on the same journey. As we enter this new space, so much will be uncertain and new. Yet many of us have seen from pregnancy how our bodies simply know how to grow a baby—deep inside us is God-given knowledge we didn't realize was there. To help develop this awareness, we offer reflections, prayers, and exercises to hone our ability to listen to ourselves, to develop our internal wisdom, and to help our bodies heal.

The chapters of the book constitute forty daily readings. Each begins with a short spiritual reading, followed by a "For the Soul" section on our understanding of a given ladder step and its relationship to new motherhood, and a "For Mind & Body" section containing practical guidance on surviving and thriving during this time. The majority of the forty days follow the thirty steps of St. John's ladder. In addition, we added days for the traditional postpartum and churching prayers, plus a few virtues and passions we feel are particularly important to mothers.

If possible, we recommend that you read the introduction, the section on Preparing for Your Postpartum Time, and Day One before you give birth. While the book will be especially helpful for new mothers over the first forty days postpartum, the exercises, prayers, and reflections serve to support both first-time and experienced mothers throughout the seasons of motherhood.

If You Remember Nothing Else . . .

As we shared with a laugh in our preface, these early days can feel like a blur. We hope that, at the very least, you can take away five main points that we refer to as our "golden rules" of motherhood. We view these ideas as the foundation that guides us in our day-to-day lives and in understanding the relationship between ourselves, our children, and God. We will refer to these "rules" throughout the book.

1. *Prayer is the way.* We can say this many ways: "When in doubt, pray," "Prayer is where we start and prayer is where we end," "Prayer is the answer." However we word it, prayer is the starting place for building a relationship with God that will allow us to survive and thrive during this time and always.

2. *Use the struggle to grow in faith and love.* Through the trials of motherhood, our soul has the opportunity to grow. As carbon is transformed through intense heat and pressure into a strong and beautiful diamond, so we too can be transformed through the struggle by God's grace and mercy. The challenges that come to us as mothers are chances for us to grow in virtue, to weed out passions, and to reach toward God. The difficulties we face can flush out the sinfulness that may have been comfortably nestled in untested corners of our soul, giving us the

opportunity to expose our wounded places and find healing through God.

3. ***Our peace brings peace.*** Our internal state, guided by our spiritual life, sets the tone for our family and home atmosphere. Do you ever notice how when you take a moment to connect to God, through prayer, gratitude, or silent contemplation, your day seems much lighter? We have. When we don't attend to our interior life, when we forget the Lord in our lives, things feel more chaotic and difficult. We've found this permeates our homes and lives, and when we have kids, it directly affects their attitude and behaviors as well. Taking care of ourselves spiritually, and in all the areas of self-care we will share, can make for a much more harmonious home life.

4. ***We are in God's hands.*** Ultimately, we must put our trust in God, for He is the one caring for us and our children. As parents, we will worry, we will be scared, and we will want to bundle our kids in bubble wrap to keep them safe at all times. However, we know we can't do this. Our children will grow, and many aspects of their lives we will not be able to control. The same is true for us. This is where we must place our faith in the Lord. He has the bird's-eye view, the close-up, and the panoramic shot. He knows, and He is above.

5. ***We start where we are.*** We may feel far from the Lord at times; we may look around and wonder where He is. Maybe we are faithfully committed to seeking the Lord but keep tripping up, and we feel discouraged. The great mercy of God is that He is always there, waiting for us to turn toward Him. If we want to find God, we need only start where we are and seek Him. At all moments we can be with the Lord, in moments of calm or chaos, even if we haven't prayed for weeks, months, or years.

Wherever we are on our journey, we can take the next step, keep moving forward toward God. Martin Luther King, Jr., famously stated, "If you can't fly, then run; if you can't run, then walk; if you can't walk, then crawl; but whatever you do, you have to keep moving forward."[2]

The First Forty Days

HISTORICAL AND PHYSICAL SIGNIFICANCE

Across time and culture, the lying-in period after childbirth has been a common prescription for the health and well-being of a mother and her baby. In Asia, Latin America, Europe, and Africa, women traditionally stayed close to their beds and homes while recovering from childbirth. Women were cared for by family, other women, or employed helpers and would do very little household work. There is an old saying that after birth a woman should spend two weeks in bed, two weeks around the bed, and another two weeks at home.

Today, standard medical advice is to take six weeks (forty-two days) to heal and recover after the birth of a child. While we are no longer encouraged to be bed-bound during this time, duties should be light and the body protected; mothers should rest and acclimate to motherhood. After six weeks women are encouraged to see their birth practitioner for a medical checkup to make sure everything is healed and the new mother is ready to resume normal activities, including intercourse and more vigorous exercise. By this time, postpartum bleeding is generally finished, breastfeeding is established, and incisions from C-sections are

---

2   Martin Luther King, Jr., "Keep Moving from This Mountain," address at Spelman College on April 10, 1960, www.kinginstitute.stanford.edu/king-papers/documents.

healed. These six weeks are also crucial for infants, allowing their immune systems to strengthen and their feeding and sleep cycles to develop a basic rhythm.

SARAH

In Germany, where I gave birth to my first child, this post-partum time is called *wochenbett*, translated as "weeks in bed/childbed." My midwives told me to stay close to bed for the first weeks. Prior to having my daughter, I couldn't imagine doing this, but after giving birth and seeing how much my body went through, how swollen, sore, and tired I was from labor and round-the-clock feedings, I was so grateful to have permission to rest.

SPIRITUAL SIGNIFICANCE

Forty days is a significant period of time in our church practices and in Scripture. We see this period of time referred to over and over in the Bible and in the canons of the Church. Rain fell for forty days during the Flood at the time of Noah. After forty days David came forward to defeat Goliath. Moses and Elijah each fasted for forty days before receiving instructions from God. After His Baptism, Jesus spent forty days in the wilderness, where He fasted and was tempted by Satan (Matt. 4:1–11). During this time the Holy Spirit was with Him. God did not abandon Jesus to be tempted alone but allowed Him to see the depth of darkness He would face and strengthened Him for it. In the same way, a new mother is not abandoned by the Church but given time to regain her strength and adjust to her new role and the new soul in her care.

In the Church we observe Great Lent for forty days and celebrate Pascha for forty days leading up to Christ's Ascension. When a person dies, we pray for the soul of the deceased, and at forty days after death we have a special service (*panikhida*) for the soul heading toward judgment. The Church cares for us throughout all of life's events and struggles, from conception to death and eternally thereafter.

As a Jewish woman who honored the Jewish laws, Mary was at home with Jesus for forty days before she brought him to be presented at the temple (Luke 2:22–24). We celebrate this Feast of the Meeting of the Lord in the Temple forty days after the Feast of Christ's Nativity (birth). As a Church, we remember Mary's purification according to Jewish law and Simeon's awe at meeting the Lord's Messiah. In honor of Mary and the wisdom of this time, new mothers are offered forty days to rest as well.

A SACRED TIME

Traditional Orthodox practice offers a mother forty days to recover before she is welcomed back to church with the churching ceremony of mother and baby. Women are given this forty-day period to allow the body and soul of the mother to recuperate while having a reprieve from sacramental preparation and the duties of church attendance. We can rest with the knowledge that the Church acknowledges the hard work we have done in bringing a child into the world and gives us time to recover and transition. It is as if we are being told, "Yes, you have been through so much and need to rest." Even for those of us who haven't gone through labor to bring our child home, the first six weeks with a new baby are incredibly demanding physically and emotionally, as well as important for bonding. This time apart from society allows the focus to be on mother, baby, family, and healing. During this time, mother and baby have space to bond, and the whole family can adjust to the new member and to everyone's new roles.

~

I think it's really beautiful that the Church reminds us to rest and be with our little ones for that time. Our culture puts so much pressure on getting back to normal, and that rest/bonding time is so important!

—EMILY, ORTHODOX MOTHER

~

Among the faithful, there are varying perspectives on how this time should be spent. Our Orthodox Faith is broad, and we have differing traditions. While we recognize that our understanding comes, in part, from the traditions of the parish in which we were raised, we write this book for all Christian women. Some women choose to stay home from activities and church; others are not happy at home and seek connection. Some priests believe that a full forty days should be taken; others leave the choice to the individual mother.

Regardless of varying traditions and individual circumstances, we acknowledge that in offering us this time, the Church recognizes the importance of these first forty days in the life of the child and the mother. With this recognition, we offer thoughts on how this postpartum time can allow for healing, spiritual growth, and a good start for our new family. While we hope this book offers comfort and support during this precious time, it is not meant as a substitute for in-person connection or professional care. Please make sure to reach out for spiritual guidance from a priest as well as medical care and advice from a doctor or midwife when needed.

In our modern world, women often feel pressure to bounce back after having a baby. We feel the need to fit into pre-pregnancy clothes and resume pre-baby lives, perhaps even to return to work a few weeks after giving birth. While this pressure may exist, we invite mothers to resist the urge to attempt to return to who they were before having a baby. We will never be the same women we were prior to the birth of this child; we will become someone new, someone richer, more seasoned. We may or may not fit into pre-pregnancy clothes quickly (or ever), but either way we can give our bodies the time they need to heal and ourselves the time we need to develop into our new role as mothers.

~

Take. It. Slow. Breathe. Hug the baby a lot. Set no expectations and just get to know the little miracle in your life. Let your body heal before jumping into the routine of daily life!
—ORTHODOX MOTHER

~

Psychiatrist Alexandra Sacks coined the term *matrescence*[3] to describe the process of a woman becoming a mother—a process that starts long before a woman births or adopts a child and continues indefinitely thereafter. We see this process as the internal evolution of self-identity, personal resources, and spiritual strength that a woman undergoes as she mothers her children. We believe that the start of this journey—when a baby is brought into a family through birth or adoption—is very important in building a strong foundation for the long road.

Starting the postpartum period with care, support, time, and forgiveness is an excellent beginning to the new relationship you will have with your baby, your partner, and yourself. We invite

---

3   Alexandra Sacks and Catherine Birndorf, *What No One Tells You: A Guide to Emotions from Pregnancy to Motherhood* (New York: Simon and Schuster Paperbacks, 2019), p. xxi.

you to let this time be a gift to yourself and your family by letting some things go and focusing on that which is truly needful. Feed yourself and your child(ren), love, pray, and rest. Everything else can wait. This is a sacred time.

SASHA

Despite my being born and raised in the Orthodox Church, the idea of a forty-day period away from church felt very foreign to me when I first became a mother. I remember feeling incredibly nervous that such an important support wouldn't be available to me for more than a month after making this life-changing transition. It seemed almost as if I were being punished or excluded. I remember feeling resentment and sadness. At the time I took it as an obedience but desperately craved a connection with the church. In many ways this book was born of the desire to have some additional spiritual connection—a spiritual regimen for the first forty days after birth. My experience of the forty days felt untethered from the supports of the Church, and I wanted to provide a different experience for other women.

An Offering

The world can seem to shrink when we first become parents. It is easy to focus entirely on our baby, reading all the development and sleep guides, or alternatively to engage in mindless entertainment in an effort to soothe away the distress of new motherhood. We are glad you found your way to this book, because we want to offer another path and a chance to deepen your spiritual life through the early days of motherhood.

We write this book from our hearts as mothers and not as

theologians. We share our faith as we understand it today, in the knowledge that we will always be striving to evolve and develop a deeper understanding of God and our relationship with Him. It is an honor for us to add our voices to the growing body of work written by Christian women for Christian women. We are so grateful for the opportunity to share our reflections, prayers, professional expertise, and hard-earned knowledge. Much like motherhood, researching and writing this book has been quite a humbling process. While we've grown through motherhood, we still struggle and fail. Our children test us, and we don't pass every trial. Delving into the depth of spiritual wisdom in St. John's *Ladder*, as well as the writings of other saints, has given us much food for our own spiritual journeys. We pray that our thoughts and offerings will give some small guidance in these early, vulnerable, and precious days.

PART I

Preparing for Your Postpartum Time

I wonder what treasures we would garner if we treated our postpartum selves with the tenderness and reverence our Church traditions accord us. Rather than approaching these weeks as a time to hurry through, if we set them aside as a unique window during which to look within, then what would happen? What if we sought not to get back to our usual self, but to lean forward into a richer new reality?

—LAURA JANSSON[1]

Before we become mothers, it is hard to comprehend what this new reality might be. While the focus of our book is the spiritual, as well as the emotional and physical, life of a mother *after* having a child, there are some practical preparations we can

---

1   Laura Jansson, *Fertile Ground: A Pilgrimage through Pregnancy* (Chesterton, IN: Ancient Faith Publishing, 2019), p. 261.

make before giving birth to pave the way for a more manageable life postpartum. Our experience of labor or the process of adoption can affect how confident and prepared we feel as we begin this journey. Setting up support beforehand, both practically and emotionally, will help no matter how we feel after bringing our baby home. There are some concrete things to consider prior to having a baby. A few we've found most helpful are outlined below.

Support

We believe we were not made to raise our babies alone. We are not superhuman. Mothers need support and practical help to thrive. We may need to humble ourselves to ask for and accept help along the way. People often want to give but don't know how. We often hear "Let me know if you need anything," or "I am happy to help." This is when we say thank you and accept the offer.

Each family has different resources, and you may or may not have helpful family nearby. If you do not have helpful friends or family close by and can afford a postpartum doula or support person, get one. Some health insurance policies cover postpartum doulas even if they don't advertise this benefit. If a postpartum doula is not in the budget, there are doulas in training who do not charge or who charge a fraction of the usual rate to get experience. Ask around before giving birth so that you have people to call when you are sleep-deprived and healing.

~

I feel so many mothers want to rush going back to church and other regular activities after the birth of their child. My advice is to relax, allow yourself to heal and rest, and above all bond and snuggle with your new little one! Ask for help with older children if your husband is not available and never turn down an offer for food or a visit!

—KRISTA, ORTHODOX MOTHER

If you had a child before, you will probably know what help you need. If you haven't been through postpartum previously, or can't think of what could help, here is a list of things you can ask for when people offer:

» Ask friends if you can call on them to come over for two hours to hold and rock your baby while you sleep, eat, or bathe.

» Enlist volunteers to come over to wash and fold the laundry, tidy up, do the dishes, or take care of other chores around the house.

» Get help with groceries—don't be shy about asking friends to pick up something for you while they are doing their own shopping.

» If you are planning a shower or registering for baby gifts, consider adding grocery or meal delivery or house cleaning to your list. These practical gifts are luxuries that can be hard to buy for ourselves but very helpful when others are offering their generosity. Online services offer grocery or meal delivery, house cleaning, and other services that could be added to your registry.

» If you have other children, ask friends if they can help with pick-up or drop-off for school/activities or take your older child(ren) for a play date.

» Ask friends to light candles for you and your family in church.

» Ask friends or the children's godparents to help in the care and shepherding of your children in church if you are not attending.

It can feel awkward or selfish to ask others to do these tasks for you, but for the giver it can be incredibly rewarding to see how much one is truly helping.

~

I think the forty days is a very important time of healing for the mother. . . . The focus should be on the mother resting and being cared for, and especially fed. I organize meals for mothers during their forty days as one step toward caring for mothers. I wish husbands were taught more about their role during this time, and encouraged to take over more housework and childcare while their wives recover. A priest's exhortation here would be especially helpful.

—JULIANA, ORTHODOX MOTHER

~

Partners

We recognize that there are many different types of families. We write this book for all mothers and families to aid them during this important time. To keep it simple, we use the term *partner* to refer to husband, baby's father, or support person.

For mothers who are raising a child on their own, setting up help, support, and a plan for getting relief so you can sleep and care for yourself will be even more important. Raising a child on your own is a difficult and noble task. It can be helpful to identify who your support people will be after birth and to reach out to members of your church as well as family and friends for help.

For mothers with partners, it is important to acknowledge this is a journey the parents will go on together. As the focus of this book is the spiritual life of a mother, we want to recognize that this development will in turn play a large role in the mother's partnership and family life. Ideally, parents will support one another in their spiritual struggles. Fathers have a crucial role in loving and supporting their partners and new babies. Throughout this book we include exercises and ideas for partner support and connection.

SASHA

As a doctor, I often tell the dads, "Your job is to take care of mom, and mom's job is to take care of the baby." That doesn't mean I don't encourage dads to be involved in the care of the baby—but I know that often in the first weeks after birth, the connection between mom and baby is still quite intimate, and dads struggle to find their role. If dads know they are supposed to be supporting mom—making sure she is eating, resting, and caring for her body after the birth—then the rest often flows from there.

⁓

Cherish this time with your newborn. And if you have older children as well, enjoy encouraging their bond as siblings. Read the lives of the saints to your children, and focus on the healing of your soul and body.

—ZOE, ORTHODOX MOTHER

⁓

Siblings

A new brother or sister is one of the greatest gifts you can give your child. Understandably, many children don't recognize this immediately. They may have ambivalent feelings about a new baby. They can be excited and happy for their new role but also anxious and scared about being replaced and losing the attention of their parents. It can be a difficult balance for all of you. We encourage you to think about how you want to greet your child after you have given birth. Plan a special role for the older sibling(s). Talk to them about what a new baby is like. Think about setting aside a few special moments daily in the early weeks to hold and talk to your older child about the new baby and give reassurance they are still loved.

SARAH

My eldest daughter was so excited for her new sister. She was seven—old enough to know what was happening and very happy to be a big sister again. On my due date, she had horrible stomach pains, and after an exam the doctor thought she might have appendicitis. We spent the day in the hospital (although not having a baby!). Medically she was fine, but with discussion and affection she was able to share how scared she was about the new baby arriving and how worried she was about losing me, my love, and my attention.

Preparing for Guests and Visitors

During this time, some women prefer to make a cocoon-like space and stay with their new family, free from the obligation of entertaining and hosting. Other women feel alone and need company. Either is fine, but it is important to know that visitors can be exhausting. Plan to discuss with your partner who you would like to have in your home, as well as your hopes and expectations. Generally, this is not a time you will want to be hosting and cooking for guests.

～

People coming to visit and holding the baby wasn't helpful and almost felt like a burden to entertain. . . . It was more helpful when people brought us something or helped clean.

—ANGELIKA, ORTHODOX MOTHER

～

SASHA

The week Sarah gave birth to her first child was the week my father died. I had been planning my visit to see Sarah in Germany for some time, and then these two amazing life changes occurred, and we decided to do it anyway. What a struggle. What Sarah needed was quiet and time with her baby—something I would not understand until my first child was born three years later. What I felt I needed was noise and distraction and not to be left alone for too long with the painful memories of that last night in hospital with my father. It was hard for both of us, and I ended up leaving early. Had we known then what we now know, neither of us would have planned that timing. The first few weeks at home with a new baby are truly sacred—full of unspeakable joy and also unimaginable difficulties and even sorrow. Taking that time for yourself and your family is so vital.

Preparation for the Day of Birth and Beyond

There is so much to be said about preparing spiritually and physically for the birth of a child that is beyond the scope of this book. To help, we include some of our favorite resources for birth preparation in our Resources section. Even so, we want to mention a few important things. Whatever your preparations, it is important to have honest conversations with your partner and birth support people about the upcoming birth, as well as about your hopes for how life will be afterward. Know that your body was created for this, and while fear of the unknown is normal, God never abandons us and will be with you in your time of need.

Many faithful friends, family members, and parishioners will be happy to pray for you during labor, birth, and early motherhood. As your time gets near, it can help to have a phone tree, email, or text group prepared to inform people when you go into labor. Ask your priest to come to read prayers over you and your child after birth. You may want to include him in your birth communication so that he can pray for you and prepare to visit.

SARAH

Each of my daughters' births was unique and is treasured in my soul. They all included moments of extreme trial that brought my girls into my arms. Although the births of my first two children were beautiful, they were trying, and I had a lot of mixed feelings to process afterward.

The birth of my third child was not without the moments of weakness, intensity, and self-doubt that are common in birth, but through it I found a renewed sense of peace and trust in the Lord. In the wee hours of the morning, when my time was upon me and I knew the hours of intensity I had yet to endure, I could only call to mind Christ as He prayed in Gethsemane. Like Him, I knew there was no way out of the difficulty before me, and like Him, I knew the reward was great. This image of Him, strong in the face of fear and finding comfort in our Father, comforted me, reminding me I was not alone.

As I labored, I prayed, especially to the Theotokos. In the laboring tub, immersed in warm water, I let my body do what it knew to do. I relaxed with each contraction and called out to the Theotokos, "Mary, Mother of God, help me to birth my baby!" With each contraction, in exquisite pain, I could feel my daughter moving down. The knowledge that she was getting closer was both terrifying and exhilarating.

When she was born at last, after all the pain and struggle, the walls of fear and hesitation crumbled, and I was filled with the pure love and joy that bringing a new soul into the world can bring. This elation lasted for weeks and weeks after she was born, its undercurrent still buoying me daily. It revealed God's grace in my life in a new way and helped me to grasp more fully that in all our struggles, as hard as they may be, we can cry out to God to be with us and help us move through to a place of faith and love.

Feeding Our Babies

Whether breastfeeding or giving a bottle, we will quickly learn that the early days with a baby involve constant feeding. There are many ways to feed a newborn: bottle, breast, formula, milk sharing. As mothers we must feed our babies in the way best suited to each of us and our newborn. We will spend a bit of time later in the book on breastfeeding as well, because it can be difficult for some, and many of us who really want to breastfeed struggle tremendously. This struggle can lead us to feel as if we've failed. We want to help you get off to the best start and to reassure you that if you choose not to or are not able to breastfeed, you will still be able to provide your baby with everything he or she needs.

SETTING UP FOR BREASTFEEDING SUCCESS

If you plan to breastfeed, the best time to start is in the hour after your baby is born. After the agitation of the birth process, babies are often wide awake, only to become quite drowsy for the next few days. If all is well with your baby, ask that he or she be placed on your chest for skin-to-skin time right after birth. Work with your birth team to help get baby nursing right away.

In the first few days after birth, your breasts don't yet have full milk. Instead they have colostrum, a thick yellow fluid that is extremely nutritious and rich in immunity-boosting and tissue-building properties. There is not much of it, and your baby will only consume a few teaspoons a day despite frequent feeding. Baby will lose weight during this time—some water weight, due to being out of the amniotic fluid, and some body weight. This is normal. Your medical team will watch baby's weight closely and also keep an eye on how yellow she is getting (called neonatal jaundice). Most babies can tolerate losing up to ten percent of their birth weight in the first week while waiting for mom's milk to come in.

Despite the fact that babies aren't getting a lot to eat during their early nursing, this time is crucial for prepping our body to know what baby needs. Every time our baby nurses, it sends a signal to our brain to know how much milk production to plan for. This is how mothers of twins and triplets can produce enough milk to nurse all their hungry little mouths. Women get into trouble here when they start to supplement with formula "just until the milk comes in." If our baby is satisfied with formula, he or she will not stimulate the breast, and our body will miss out on knowing how much baby is needing. Some circumstances require that we supplement with formula (e.g., certain medications, or a need for mother and baby to be separated for the first few days of life). In these cases we make the sign of the cross and put our faith in God that we are taking care of our baby as we best can.

To help with the actual process of nursing, we recommend a few things. First, in the early days while baby is still so tiny and floppy, set yourself up well with pillows and get baby's mouth and your breast into a good position. This makes a tremendous difference. Most hospitals have lactation consultants who can assist, and there are also lots of private and sometimes even public pay options for when we are home.

Second, try to become attuned to early hunger cues. Hunger cues—opening the mouth, sticking out the tongue, sucking noises, mouth movements, eating fingers, and turning the head from side to side—are early signs that our baby is ready to eat. Waiting until our baby cries from hunger may make it harder for him or her to settle and latch on.

Third, a deep and secure latch is arguably the most important thing to learn for successful and less painful nursing. Many videos and online resources teach what this looks and feels like and offer troubleshooting help.

Finally, know that this is not easy, even if we were successful before. In these early days we, as well as our baby, are learning, all while our body is still changing and healing. Don't be afraid to get help. It can make all the difference. God loves us more than we can ever comprehend and will give us what we need—even if it doesn't appear to be exactly what we asked for. If we aim to breastfeed and it doesn't work, we are blessed to have other ways to nourish our baby's body while we get on with the important work of nourishing their souls.

It's Almost Time

In giving birth, we join generations of women who have become mothers and whose bodies have grown and birthed babies. As we prepare for and give birth, we can give thanks for our strength and the amazing body God has given us with which to bring life into the world. We want to share with you a selection from a well-loved prayer you may use during pregnancy and leading up to birth. We hope it will bring much comfort.

✛ ORTHODOX PRAYER FOR ✛ PREGNANT MOTHER AND UNBORN CHILD[2]

O All-Merciful Christ our God, look down and protect me, Thy handmaiden, from fear and from evil spirits that seek to destroy the work of Thy hands. And when my hour and time is come, deliver me by Thy grace. Look with compassionate eye and deliver me, Thy handmaiden, from pain. Lighten mine infirmity in the time of my travail and grant me fortitude and strength for birth giving, and hasten it by Thine almighty help. For this is Thy glorious work, the power of Thine omnipotence, the work of Thy grace and tender-heartedness. Amen.

A Note on Baptism

In the Orthodox Church we practice infant baptism. In baptism we put on Christ and receive the grace of God. It is this grace

---

2   "Orthodox Prayers for Pregnant Mother and Unborn Child," The Saint Gregory Palamas Outreach, accessed April 30, 2020, http://www.saintgregoryoutreach.org/2012/02/orthodox-prayers-pregnancy.html.

that will guide, form, and protect our children as they grow. It is grace that will help to shape their hearts and minds. We give our children this gift from their infancy so they can know God, participate in His sacraments, and grow in their own faith.

As they grow, our children will make their own choices. At some point in their lives, they will choose either to continue in Christ or to go another way. We can pray that bringing our children to God from their earliest days and bringing them up in the Lord will help to guide and shape them in such a way that they will stay close to God throughout their lives.

Baptism is a beautiful gift for our children. It brings a baby into the sacramental life of the Church to receive life-giving communion and to become part of the body of Christ. We recommend talking to your priest and planning the baptism as soon as your baby is born.

The Importance of Self-Care

Proper self-care enables you to live generously out of your abundance rather than begrudgingly out of your scarcity.

—HANNAH VASQUEZ[3]

We hope you are able to read this before giving birth, but if not, we are glad you are reading it now. Better still, read this before you give birth and then again and again afterward. We can't stress enough the importance of self-care, as we have learned the hard way how crucial it is to a healthy and capable mother and a well-cared-for family.

Self-Care

The safety announcement on an airplane reminds passengers to put on their own oxygen mask before helping others with theirs. For us as caretakers, trying to live in imitation of our Lord, it might seem counterintuitive to put our own needs ahead of

---

3   Hannah Vasquez, "Self-Care for the Orthodox Mama—Part 1," *All These Things* podcast, June 8, 2020, https://www.ancientfaith.com/podcasts/all-thesethings/self_care_for_the_orthodox_mama_part_1.

others. However, without our own oxygen mask on, we won't stay conscious long enough to help anyone else, and we will all be lost. Our ultimate example of sacrifice, Jesus, slept and ate and took care of His basic needs while caring for those around Him. He left the care of the multitudes to others so He could go off and pray in the desert. He slept in the bottom of the boat while the storm raged around Him. When we become mothers, it becomes harder to remember to care for ourselves, but it is even more crucial now as our well-being affects our children. *Our peace brings peace.* If we don't have our own needs attended to, we will not be fit to attend to others.

Maybe it was easier during pregnancy to allow others to care for us or to pamper ourselves—getting a bit more sleep, eating extra healthy food, or accepting a seat from a kind stranger. It can be jarring when all the focus goes from us, as pregnant women, to the new baby. It is important to remember that we are still the lifeline for our baby. We have gone through a lot emotionally, physically, and spiritually to bring our baby into the world, and we have only just begun. We will need stamina to care for our child in all the ways he will need.

We aren't talking about self-care in superficial ways, such as getting a manicure or spa treatment or going shopping with friends, although these can be enjoyable breaks. Rather, we mean tending to our needs just as Jesus tended to His—feeding ourselves, getting rest, caring for our bodies. This also means recognizing the deeper aspects of who we are, what we want in life, and how we are building a foundation to sustain us through the wisdom and love of God.

Throughout the book, we touch on the basic elements of self-care that will help us thrive as women and mothers. Here, we wish to give a general overview of concepts that will appear again later. We view self-care as holistic, taking care of ourselves in soul, body, and mind. We are spiritual beings and as such must care for our souls. We do this in many ways, and as Christians we are given practices to help us along. Reading Scripture, attending services, going to confession, fasting, receiving communion, prayer, stillness, and connection to our faith communities are all ways we care for our souls.

Physical self-care focuses on caring for our body and keeping our needs met so that we can be strong to carry out our purpose. We also need to focus on our mental and emotional self-care. This includes feeding our friendships, fostering our interests and hobbies, being clear on our purpose, and exercising our intellect. As many of these activities are limited right after birth, we focus throughout the book on the ones that are most accessible during these early days.

We thought it important to discuss this area in a bit more detail so you can plan and prepare for how you will care for yourself, making time for spiritual practice and physical, mental, and emotional self-care that will sustain you once your baby arrives. Each chapter offers prayers, practices, and exercises to help you do this. We also highly recommend getting a journal for this time period. We have included many writing/journaling exercises throughout the book.

Spiritual Self-Care

PRAYER

If asked to summarize this book in one word, it would be "pray." All the things we've learned and share here come back to prayer. *Prayer is the way.* This is our first golden rule because it lays the foundation for everything else. Prayer is going to be an important part of your new life as a mother, particularly as you now have the responsibility for another soul and a duty to pray for your child. Taking time to thank, reach out, and be in stillness with God will help you develop the fortitude and internal strength that motherhood requires. Prayer will help you find peace in the stressful, difficult, and fearful moments. Prayer will see you through the times of sickness, sleeplessness, and worry, and will give you grace in the face of adversity.

For a new mother, finding time to pray can be challenging. Most likely your waking and sleeping schedules will shift quickly and drastically, and if you had a morning and evening prayer rule, it can feel close to impossible to find the same rhythm with a baby right away. We offer many ways throughout the book to weave prayer into the fabric of your days with a new baby.

Something you can do now is to prepare a comfortable chair for feeding and rocking your baby, since much of a newborn's life consists of feeding and sleeping. A rocker, glider, or rocking recliner will be very helpful in both breast- and bottle-feeding, and it will continue to be useful for many years of holding, rocking, and reading to your little one. Put a small table near the chair with a bottle of water or a pitcher and a cup so you can hydrate yourself easily. Place an icon of the Theotokos in your line of vision. She will be a wonderful companion in the late nights, watching over you and your baby. Seeing her will be a good reminder that you are not alone but part of generations of women who have cared for babies. You can sing to her, talk to her, and share all your hopes and fears in these early moments. You may find that having a few such spots throughout the house will be helpful. We hope one of these spots will have a space for this book.

Physical Self-Care

NUTRITION

Nourishing our postpartum body is a tremendously important part of self-care and gives us physical energy to care for a newborn. Keeping ourselves well fed and hydrated will assist in healing, building milk supply, stabilizing mood, and strengthening our immune system. If breastfeeding, we need to drink even more water to stay hydrated. We recommend stashing a few full water bottles where baby will be fed. During this time, it is best to limit caffeine and alcohol as both can disrupt sleep and increase anxiety.

In general, we both believe in the benefit of eating a diet based, as much as possible, on whole and unprocessed foods. We encourage lots of healthy fats and fresh fruits and vegetables. In addition, consuming plenty of omega-3s from fish and nuts, as well as supplements, has been associated with decreased levels of depression and anxiety, which affect many women postpartum. These fatty acids are also helpful in nurturing our baby's developing brain.

If it is not already part of your little home church, we recommend getting a bottle of holy water and a small supply of holy bread to use for your postpartum time. These are beneficial additions to any home church, and consuming them is a lovely tradition for children as well. It is a beautiful and tangible part of our spiritual life when we are not able to be in church or receive Holy Communion.

Cooking extra portions and meals to freeze and enjoy postpartum is enormously helpful. Some communities also set up meal trains to schedule homemade food deliveries from family and friends. If someone doesn't offer this for you, consider making one yourself, putting meals on your baby shower list, or suggesting a meal whenever someone asks if you need anything. There are several helpful websites to make coordinating meal trains easier. (We've listed our favorite in the Resources section.) If grocery delivery is not part of your normal life, many services offer a free trial period you can use during your first forty days to relieve yourself of having to get out the door with a newborn.

SLEEP, REJUVENATION & REST

Getting sleep is one of the most important aspects of good health for a new mother, but it can also be one of the most difficult to come by in early motherhood. Some babies may sleep for multiple-hour stretches, while others may wake every hour in the beginning. In the first weeks, give yourself permission to rest as often as you are able. Ask for help. Have others help with feeding, or after a feeding let your partner or a visitor take care of the baby so you can rest. Just resting is important. Some women find it hard to sleep during the day no matter how tired they are. If this is true for you, rest anyway. Even simply putting your feet up in the first few weeks will help with healing and mood.

Developing good sleep habits while caring for a newborn is so important. It can be tempting to stay up once the baby is finally asleep. While having a few moments to ourselves, or with our spouse or other children, is important and precious, let that happen only occasionally, and guard your sleep carefully. We can take care of ourselves best by planning to be in bed for the ten or so hours during the nighttime that baby is sleeping. Set yourself up so you don't need to move around too much (and thus wake up fully) when you tend to baby. That might mean keeping a change of diapers nearby and an extra pair of pajamas or a swaddle ready. If you are bottle-feeding, make sure bottles are set up to mix formula easily. If you have other children, see if your partner can be responsible for them during the night and first thing in the morning, so you can get as much sleep as possible overnight. Sleep is vital not only for healing but for coping. With all the emotional changes and stimulus a new baby brings, we will need all the coping help we can get!

CARING FOR YOUR BODY

Giving birth is often described as one of the most intense, difficult, and amazing experiences a woman's body will go through. After birth, our joints, muscles, ligaments, and organs will feel out of place and strange. The fullness of our pregnant belly is replaced by organs needing to find their way back to a new space. We find that our muscles feel different. In the first days it is best to rest in bed as much as possible and allow our body to heal.

When you're ready to start moving, go slowly. In the beginning, exercising will not feel as it did in the past. It is important to rebuild our pelvic floor, stabilize our core, and lay the foundation for future exercise and health. Many communities offer classes especially targeting the needs of our newly postpartum bodies. We will discuss this at certain places throughout the book, and you can also see our Resources section for suggestions.

Our body is a "temple of the Holy Spirit" (1 Cor. 6:19) that, for many of us, just grew another human life. We can take moments to tend to ourselves, taking notice of what our body needs just as we are alert to the needs of our baby's body. We can go easy on ourselves and thank God for the miracle of our body.

Unfortunately, we live in a culture with unreasonable beauty standards, where women's bodies are judged as a measure of worth. We can remember that we are strong and amazing, even when we don't recognize our post-baby body. Our body may feel tired, deflated, weary, and bruised, but we will heal and regain strength with time. We are beautiful women who have fulfilled the hope of life. Our eyes may not see the flush of love in our cheeks or the regal strength in this body that has borne another, but it is there.

Mental and Emotional Self-Care

CONNECTION

We are communal beings who need connection to God and one another, especially in times of need, change, and transition. The first weeks with a new baby are a time when a woman especially needs to be supported. As you heal and life begins to normalize, it is important to connect with loved ones, your partner, fellow parishioners, and other mothers who can share, guide, and laugh with you. If you have a hard time reaching out, it might be helpful to look up some new mother groups (often run through hospitals, community centers, or libraries) that you might attend after your baby is born. These groups provide a chance for new moms to get support from one another, and they often result in lasting friendships. If possible, research these groups before you give birth so you know what your options are before you need them.

Although you may not be going to church during this time, God is always with you. Even if you are alone with this new baby, remember that Jesus taught, "Where two or three are gathered together in My name, I am there in the midst of them" (Matt. 18:20). We are never alone; just being a new mother gives us a tremendous amount in common with many women we have never met who are likely wanting connection just as we are.

~

Having company from other Orthodox women was essential for me in this period of time, when I couldn't find spiritual consolation in the church. I would definitely encourage women to organize a meal train for their friends who are in their forty days, to visit them, and to stay in touch as much as possible.

—DIACONITSA CATHERINE, ORTHODOX MOTHER

~

PURPOSE

When the days are long and life with a baby feels monotonous (sleep, eat, diaper, repeat), remembering our purpose can help to ground us and give us strength and clarity. Often women define their purpose by their roles: daughter, sister, friend, wife, mother, homemaker, professional. These roles can help a woman define her identity, but we should also remember our true calling as Christians. Our ultimate purpose in life is to worship and connect with God, living out our lives toward salvation. All of these roles can aid us in doing this, but whenever the deeper questions arise, we can point to this higher calling.

While our roles and occupations before becoming mothers may continue to be important to us, in moments when we struggle or feel adrift we can remember the words of St. Theophan the Recluse: "Of all holy works, the education of children is the most holy."[4] As mothers, we take on a new role and purpose: to teach and guide our children in the ways of the Lord. This is echoed in the words of Fr. John Breck, who wrote *The Sacred Gift of Life*: "For the first responsibility of parents—in fact, their most basic

---

4   St. Theophan the Recluse, *Raising Them Right* (Chesterton, IN: Ancient Faith Publishing, 2005), p. 84.

vocation—is to reflect to their children the image of God, an image of truth, faithfulness, integrity and love."[5] As we go forward, we can hold these words in our heart, knowing that our purpose is a holy one and our goal is to teach our children to love and know God.

---

5   Fr. John Breck, "The Sacredness of Newborn Life," In Communion, accessed April 30, 2020, https://incommunion.org/2004/10/21/the-sacredness-of-newborn-life/.

PART II

A Mother Is Born

The most difficult part of birth is the first year afterwards. It is the year of travail—when the soul of a woman must birth the mother inside her. The emotional labor pains of becoming a mother are far greater than the physical pains of birth; these are the growing surges of your heart as it pushes out selfishness and fear and makes room for sacrifice and love.

—JOY KUSEK[1]

1   Joy M. Kusek, "Making Room for Love." *The Joy of This* (blog), July 29, 2010, https://thejoyofthis.com/2010/07/29/making-room-for-love/.

Birth

A New Life

A woman, when she is in labor, has sorrow because her hour has come; but as soon as she has given birth to the child, she no longer remembers the anguish, for joy that a human being has been born into the world.

—JOHN 16:21

You're here! You made it! The long-awaited time has arrived. You hold in your arms a new soul born into your life. You have become a mother! Whether you are a mother by adoption, vaginal birth, C-section, or after a long struggle with infertility—you are a mother. What a great blessing and joyous event! Congratulations!

For the Soul

If your priest is able to come and read prayers over you and your baby, embrace this beautiful and solemn moment to hold your baby to your chest, thanking God and asking Him for love, for-giveness, and protection of the new life in your arms. Below is the first of three sets of prayers prescribed by the Orthodox Church to be read over mother and child during the first forty days of a child's life.

✝ PRAYERS ON THE FIRST DAY AFTER ✝ A WOMAN HAS GIVEN BIRTH TO A CHILD[2]

O Master, Lord Almighty, who heal every sickness and every weakness, heal also this Your handmaiden, N., who today has given birth, and raise her from the bed on which she lies. For, according to the words of the Prophet David, in sins were we conceived, and all are defiled before You. Pre-serve her and this child which she has borne. Cover her with the shelter of Your wings from this day until her final end, through the prayers of the Most-Holy Theotokos and all the saints. For blessed are You unto the ages of ages. Amen.

O Master, Lord our God, who were born of our Most-Holy Sovereign Lady, the Theotokos and Ever-Virgin Mary, who, as an infant, lay in a manger and were carried as a little child: have mercy on this Your handmaiden who has given birth today to this child. Forgive her all her transgressions, both voluntary and involuntary, and protect her from every oppression of the devil. Preserve the infant who was born of her from every spell, from every cruel thing, from every storm or adversity, and from evil spirits, whether of the day or of the night. Keep this woman under Your mighty

---

2   Adapted from St. Tikhon's Seminary Press, *The Great Book of Holy Needs, Expanded and Supplemented,* vol. 1, *The Holy Mysteries* (South Canaan, PA: St. Tikhon's Seminary Press, 1998), pp. 3–5.

hand and grant her a speedy recovery, and purify her from uncleanness, and heal her sufferings. Grant her health and strength of soul and body, and surround her with bright and radiant angels, and preserve her from every approach of invisible spirits: from sickness and infirmity, from jealousy and envy, and from the evil eye. And have mercy on her and on the infant according to Your great mercy, and cleanse her from bodily uncleanness and the various afflictions of her womb. And by Your quick mercy lead her to recovery of her humbled body. Grant that the infant who has been born of her may worship in the earthly temple which You have prepared for the glorification of Your Holy Name. . . .

O Lord, our God, who were well-pleased to come down from heaven and be born of the Holy Theotokos and Ever-Virgin Mary for the salvation of sinners, who know the frailty of human nature: According to the multitude of Your compassions, forgive Your handmaid, *N.*, who has given birth today. For You have said, O Lord: "Be fruitful and multiply, fill the earth and subdue it." Therefore, we, Your servants, pray, and having boldness on account of Your forbearing love for mankind, with fear we cry out to Your Holy Name: Look down from heaven and behold the feebleness of us who are condemned, and forgive this, Your handmaiden *N.*, and the whole household into which this infant has been born, and all who have touched her, and all here present, forgive all of them, inasmuch as You are a good God and the Lover of Mankind; for You alone have the power to forgive sins, through the prayers of the Most-Holy Theotokos and of all Your saints. Amen.

In these prayers we hear the call for healing, protection, and forgiveness. Much of the language of the prayers is familiar to Orthodox Christians, but there are a few areas that merit more discussion. In our conversations and research with other Orthodox mothers, some shared the prayer's language caused feelings of confusion and shame. Given this, we felt it important to look at the prayers[3] and try to shed some light on their context and meaning within our Orthodox tradition.[4] We hope that our understanding will help future mothers to feel the love and care the Church offers in this early period and dispel any shame felt around the amazing process of bringing a new life into the world.

The three prayers offered for the mother and her infant after birth are the first step toward the child's baptism and chrismation. If our ultimate role and purpose is to find salvation in life eternal with God, then we see that the Church reaches out to the mother and child on the first day of life, welcoming the infant into her arms and laying the spiritual foundation for the child's relationship with God.

At the time of Christ's birth, the laws of Moses (Leviticus 1—27) detailed how Jews were to worship God, how they could become "impure" or "unclean," and the ways that a woman or man could ritually cleanse herself or himself to become pure once again. According to the Mosaic laws, one could become ritually unclean if one came in contact with bodily fluids, dead bodies, or bodies with an illness such as leprosy. In this unclean

---

3   We are looking at the prayers used in the *The Great Book of Needs*. Different jurisdictions use prayers that contain varied translations and wording.

4   In our research we've come across varying perspectives and voices throughout the writings of the Church Fathers as well as contemporary thinkers. Much has been written to help dispel the notion that postpartum women are viewed as "impure" in our Christian understanding. Still, understanding varies depending on local culture and tradition.

state one could not enter the temple and offer sacrifice, which was a main way Jews communed with God. Remaining in a state of ritual uncleanness was to cut oneself off from God.[5] To cleanse oneself, one would enter a ritual bath, called a *mikveh*,[6] and could also give a burnt offering to the temple.

Due to the blood and fluids of childbirth as well as the sacredness of giving birth, Jewish custom viewed the mother and those in contact with her as "impure."[7] This was not considered a moral impurity but a bodily impurity. Forty days after giving birth, Mary was able to return to the temple after "purifying" herself in a ritual bath and offering a burnt sacrifice.

Many of our Christian beliefs grew from Jewish roots, and there are echoes of Jewish tradition in our prayers, worship, and ritual. Even so, a fundamental difference in our beliefs is that Christ's death and Resurrection released us from Jewish Law. Christ came not to destroy the Law, but to fulfill it (Matt. 5:17), and because of the Resurrection, we are not bound by the laws of Moses. As Christians, we believe we are renewed through Jesus Christ, and the law and understanding of ritual impurity have been transformed. Baptism is the only purification Christians need, and it is performed only once. We do not ritually cleanse our bodies; instead, we renew our baptism through repentance and confession to heal our souls from our sins.

To live a truly Christian life is to be in a perpetual state of

5   Joe M. Sprinkle, "Clean, Unclean," Bible Study Tools, accessed April 30, 2019, https://www.biblestudytools.com/dictionaries/bakers-evangelical-dictionary/clean-unclean.html.

6   Beth Wenger, "Mikveh," *Jewish Women: A Comprehensive Historical Encyclopedia*, Jewish Women's Archive, accessed April 30, 2020, https://jwa.org/encyclopedia/article/mikveh.

7   Susan Handelman, "On the Essence of Ritual Impurity," Chabad.org, accessed April 30, 2020, https://www.chabad.org/theJewishWoman/article_cdo/aid/1542/jewish/On-the-Essence-of-Ritual-Impurity.htm.

asking for forgiveness, with the unceasing prayer of the heart ever at our lips: "Lord Jesus Christ, have mercy on me, a sinner." At the moment of immense labor and the bringing forth of a new soul, the same is true. Childbirth is not a sin, nor does it make us impure, but we remain sinners, and when birthing a new soul, as in all other moments of prayer, we ask to be cleansed of our sin. What better time in our lives can there be to lay our cares upon the Lord, to repent of our sins, than when we have pushed our body to its limits, brought forth new life, and come so close to the glory of God? In these precious moments after birth, we are naked before the Lord, our souls are wide open, and we pray that the purifying love of God will wash us and allow us to cross the threshold of motherhood safely, cleansed in soul and body.

The late Orthodox writer and priest Fr. Alexander Schmemann devotes a chapter of his book on baptism, *Of Water and the Spirit*, to these prayers. In understanding the continual request for purification and forgiveness, he says, "we must recognize that we are created to be one with God, but due to our fallen nature we have strife and struggle."[8] Father Schmemann writes that the prayers reveal:

> *Joy at that event, at the entrance of another child of God into God's 'marvelous light,' yet also—and therefore—sadness about the corruption of the world by sin . . . and if these prayers are, first of all, a cry for forgiveness, it is because only divine forgiveness—given and fulfilled in Christ and His Coming—can purify that joy, restore it to its fullness, make this beginning of life the beginning also of salvation and redemption.*[9]

---

8   Alexander Schmemann, *Of Water and the Spirit* (London: SPCK, 1976), p. 136.
9   Ibid. p. 137.

In these prayers, we see the recognition of our fallen nature. We are all subject to sin. We can be cleansed of our sins through the divine love and redemptive forgiveness offered us through Jesus Christ. We are reminded of the maternal perfection of the Theotokos in giving birth to Jesus. By her example and intercessions, the new mother and child are offered the greatest gift of love and salvation through the life of the Church and Jesus Christ. With these prayers we are invited, as is our child, into the shelter of the protection of the Lord.

SARAH

When I became a mother, I was in a foreign country. My parish priest and I communicated in German, a mutual second language. My churching was organized by a friend and unexpectedly cancelled as my priest had an emergency. We moved back to the U.S. when my daughter was nine weeks old, and her baptism occurred a few days after our arrival. My childhood priest read all the prayers for us at the entrance of the church and churched us prior to her baptism. I didn't know about the prayers for mother at birth or the naming prayers. I felt great relief in hearing them and knowing my daughter and I were being blessed and welcomed into the life of the Church.

With my later children, I looked forward to the prayers the Church offered for new mothers and babies. I found the language of the prayers familiar, similar to so many of the prayers and services I had known throughout my life: comfort in asking for help, healing, forgiveness, and protection of myself and my infants. When my parish priest read the first-day prayers on the day of my second daughter's birth, I was flooded with a great feeling of relief. I shed tears of joy and repentance as I moved into my new reality as a mother of two.

➤ PREPARATION NOTE ◀

The naming prayers are the next set of prayers, traditionally said for the child on the eighth day of life. Discuss with your priest whether he will be able to say these prayers for your infant on or near the eighth day after baby's birth.

For Mind & Body

LIFE AFTER BIRTH

When a child enters the world, a sacredness surrounds those initial hours. After the rush of birth and the medical examinations, often the new family feels a sense of calm. There is nothing quite like holding your infant asleep against your body, the familiar hearts now beating in two separate chests. Each birth is unique; the experience varies from mother to mother, and even from birth to birth. Some are flooded with feelings of joy and ecstasy, while some are too exhausted from the hard work of labor even to hold their infant. Many of us feel an overwhelming sense of relief to have made it through the birth and finally to be holding our baby, while in awe of the whole experience and the new life in our arms.

Whether you gave birth in a hospital, birthing center, at home, or somewhere in between, your medical providers most likely have given you a sense of what to expect and when to be concerned. During this first day you will be experiencing uterine contractions as your uterus works to shrink back to its regular shape. New mothers are often not prepared for the amount of bleeding that occurs after giving birth. Bleeding will continue over the next several weeks. Be sure to call your healthcare provider if you are passing clots larger than a golf ball or soaking a pad within an hour.

Depending on your birth experience, you may have medications and will certainly have many natural hormones flowing through your body. All of these, combined with the hard work your body has gone through and the emotions of meeting your child, will leave you exhausted and emotional. It is normal to laugh one moment and cry the next.

Finally, if you are reading this book after going through the adoption process, we recognize a lot of the above may not apply. Your journey to motherhood may have started a bit differently, but the spiritual strength needed to raise your child will be the same. Congratulations to all who hold new life in their arms!

DAY 2

Renunciation

Leaving the Past Behind

*To all who are diligent to have their name inscribed in the
book of life in Heaven, the present book points out the best
path. Journeying by this way, we shall find that this book
is an unerring guide to those who follow it, keeping them
unharmed from every stumbling stone. And it sets before us a
fixed ladder leading from things earthly to the Holy of Holies;
it makes manifest the God of love, who stands upon its summit.... And so, I entreat you, let us climb with zeal and faith
up this spiritual and Heaven-scaling ladder, the beginning of
which is renunciation of all earthly things, and the end, the
God of love.*

—PROLOGUE TO *THE LADDER OF DIVINE ASCENT*[10]

---

10   St. John Climacus, *The Ladder of Divine Ascent* (Boston, MA: Holy Trans-
     figuration Monastery, 1991), p. xlv.

The first renunciation is that of material things, the second that of the passions, the third that of ignorance.

—SAINT THALASSIOS THE LIBYAN[11]

Love is the fruit of prayer. . . . For it is alike when a man prays veraciously and when he dies from this world; this means that he denies himself, and this means continually living in prayer.

—SAINT ISAAC THE SYRIAN[12]

For the Soul

Renunciation, defined by *The Merriam-Webster Dictionary* as "ascetic self-denial,"[13] is the first rung of St. John of Climacus's *Ladder of Divine Ascent*. While we emphasize that caring for ourselves as mothers is important for our well-being and will allow us to best care for our children, we admit that caring for a newborn is often an act of self-denial.

Your awareness of what this means in practice with a newborn may be growing. Day two of your baby's life means you have experienced a night together—likely waking up at all hours and possibly not sleeping at all. This is real. The afterpains of birth are real, the beautiful sleeping child is real, the massive change in your life is real.

In her book *The Spiritual Child*, psychologist Lisa Miller calls

---

11 St. Thalassios the Libyan, "On Love, Self-Control and Life in Accordance with the Intellect," 3.23, *The Philokalia: The Complete Text (Vol. 2)*, compiled by St. Nikodimos of the Holy Mountain and St. Makarios of Corinth, trans. and ed. G.E.H Palmer, Phillip Sherrard, and Kallistos Ware (London: Faber and Faber, 1981), p. 320.

12 Isaac of Nineveh, *Mystic Treatise,* trans. Arent Jan Wensinck (Amsterdam: Royal Academy for Arts and Sciences, 1923), p. 319.

13 "Renunciation," Merriam-Webster.com, accessed April 30, 2020, https://www.merriam-webster.com/dictionary/renunciation?src=search-dict-box.

this act of renunciation "ego-death." Ego-death is a "surrender of control and vanity that actually makes us *more*."[14] In caring for a newborn, we realize that we cannot control the new being in our lives. Babies have around-the-clock needs and are unpredictable, especially in the beginning of life. As we learn more about our child and her unique personality, things will stabilize a bit, but our lives are changed forever. We, too, are changing and, as Miller says, we are becoming "more" as we grow as parents. She also likens parenthood to the ascetic struggle:

> *Parenthood is a spiritual pilgrimage however you travel the path. Imagine the solitary monk making his way to the mountaintop in search of enlightenment: The hard work and austerity, the steep climb with its trials and setbacks, uncertainty in place of control, the disorientation as the self or ego dissolves into a spirit that is no longer self-centered but now exists for something larger and more precious than the self— your child.*[15]

In the dissolution of ego, something greater grows. In embracing self-denial, we make the choice to grow stronger in love and conviction. *Use the struggle to grow in faith and love.* We have a clearer purpose and understanding of what is truly important in our lives. We will touch on this more in later days, but for now, consider renunciation as an invitation to enter into this new part of life while disengaging from the world of cares outside our doors.

---

14   Lisa Miller, *The Spiritual Child* (New York: Picador, 2016), p. 320.
15   Ibid. p. 318.

SARAH

Having my first baby before most of my friends had children, I wasn't aware of new-baby culture, books, and ideas. I read books about birth, but very little about what would happen once the baby arrived. This added to the eye-opening experience of suddenly holding my precious daughter and discovering that she didn't want to sleep for more than forty-five minutes at a time. If she wasn't nestled on one of us, she was sure to let everyone know how unhappy she was about it. I spent those first weeks in a sleepless state of semi-reality, vacillating between complete love and joy, and fear that I would never sleep again. I felt at the complete mercy of this new role and the child in my life.

The good news is, I did get to sleep again. My thoughtful sister-in-law sent me the book *The Happiest Baby on the Block*, which helped me to understand the concept of the months after birth being like a fourth trimester, where my baby was still growing so much and would greatly benefit from womblike conditions. By four or five months, there was a big shift, and we started to have some relief.

For Mind & Body

TAKING CARE OF OUR TEMPLE

Our bodies go through so much in pregnancy, birth, and caring for a baby. Because we think this physical exertion is also part of our spiritual growth, and learning to care for our body is honoring the temple God has given us, we suggest exercises throughout the book to aid our healing and to help us find peace with our bodies in this postpartum time and beyond.

Breathing is one of our automatic body functions, in that we breathe without thinking, but it is also one of the automatic functions we can readily control. This is important because breathing consciously (focusing and controlling our breath) allows us to access our parasympathetic nervous system, the system responsible for calming us down. Activating this system releases relaxing hormones, slows our heart rate, lowers blood pressure, lowers stress, and can help us let go and fall asleep.

Calling on God in moments of trial is essential for us as Christians. By being present in our struggles and choosing to respond with kindness and compassion, we can create new habits that will support us in difficult moments. Below is an exercise to help you to calm yourself and accept where you are in each moment.

➤ EXERCISE ◄

Focused Belly Breathing with the Jesus Prayer

Take a look at how your baby breathes when he is sleeping. Likely you will appreciate his belly softly rising and falling with each breath. This is how we breathe most naturally and comfortably. However, through chronic tension and rushing, most of us have learned to breathe into our chests. This can be a hard habit to break, even for the duration of a short exercise. We recommend you lie on your back, perhaps next to your sleeping little one or even with her snoozing on your chest. You could also try this while breastfeeding once you get the hang of it.

If possible, place one hand on your chest and one hand on your belly. Notice your breathing as it is. Slowly begin to bring more breath into the hand on your belly. Don't worry if it doesn't come easily; just focus on breathing deeply and aiming to fill the lower belly as you can. Once you develop a rhythm, you can begin to link the words of the "Jesus prayer" to the breath—"Lord Jesus Christ, Son of God, have mercy on me, a sinner." If you are able and find it soothing, you can say "Lord Jesus Christ, Son of God" on the inhalation and "have mercy on me, a sinner" on the exhalation.

Do this for three to five rounds whenever you feel the need, or when you are overwhelmed or anxious. Keep the Jesus prayer close and say it as often as it comes to mind. This practice helps calm us and strengthens our prayer life, keeping us connected with our main source of strength— our Lord and God and Savior Jesus Christ.

Focusing on breath and becoming present in our body releases tension and brings emotions to the surface. This is especially likely after birth, when we may not have had a moment to connect to ourselves or check in with our bodies. It is normal to feel emotional or to cry during this time. If that is the case now, don't worry. Ask for a hand to hold or a hug from your support person. Letting ourselves actually *feel* our emotions, rather than trying to distract ourselves or push painful emotions away, is an important part of the healing process.[16]

---

16 Hear the full guided version of this exercise on our podcast, *A Sacred Beginning*, on ancientfaith.com.

DAY 3

Detachment

Learning to Go Beyond Ourselves

This is a great toil, very great indeed, with much unseen suffering. . . . But let us who are weak and passionate have the courage to offer our infirmity and natural weakness to Christ with unhesitating faith, and confess it to Him; and we shall be certain to obtain His help.

—SAINT JOHN CLIMACUS[17]

Do not lay up for yourselves treasures on earth, where moth and rust destroy and where thieves break in and steal; but lay up for yourselves treasures in heaven, where neither moth nor rust destroys and where thieves do not break in and steal. For where your treasure is, there your heart will be also.

—MATTHEW 6:19–21

The one who is perfect in love and has reached the summit of detachment knows no distinction between one's own and

17   *Ladder*, p. 6.

another's, between faithful and unfaithful, between slave and freeman, or indeed between male and female. But . . . having risen above the tyranny of the passions and looking to the one nature of men he regards all equally and is equally disposed toward all. For in him there is neither Greek nor Jew, neither male nor female, neither slave nor freeman, but Christ is everything and in everything.

—SAINT MAXIMOS THE CONFESSOR[18]

For the Soul

Hopefully we find you curled up, holding a cup of something warm and nourishing, with a sleeping baby on your chest as you find a few minutes to read. This third day after birth often finds us in the initial awe of getting to know our baby. For many of us, these early days of mothering are about fostering a secure and loving attachment between parents and baby. Why then would we be looking at de-attachment in the context of early motherhood? This is not the sort of detachment we mean. Rather, we want to reflect on spiritual detachment, which is the recognition that we were not created for this world, and while we live in the world, we are not *of* the world. Motherhood presents us with many opportunities to grasp this concept.

In the first days after the birth of a child, we have a definite sense of detachment from time and from the world outside our door. We are not participating in our daily lives in the same way; we even detach from our church for a time. We may also experience an internal shift, detaching from our pre-baby self as we make space to grow into our self as mother.

---

18   St. Maximos the Confessor, *The Selected Writings of St. Maximos the Confessor* (Mahwah, NJ: Paulist Press, 1985), p. 51.

As we touched upon with renunciation in the last chapter, this is the beginning of detaching from selfishness. As Christians we should always strive to place others' needs ahead of, or at the very least alongside, our own. Having a helpless newborn in our arms brings this discipline to a whole new level. This can be hard to accept. It is a rewiring that can take a long time for many of us. As we learn how to put the needs of our baby at the forefront, we grow stronger and clearer in purpose, and we are better able to guide and support our children as they grow.

Becoming a mother involves a big learning curve. Likely we've lived our lives mostly for ourselves before having children, perhaps learning to compromise more in being a wife or in various capacities in our work or social commitments. As a mother of a newborn we are asked to detach much more from our own immediate needs and wants, putting them in second place for a time in order to care for a growing family. God in His wisdom starts us out with adorable helpless infants who require constant attention and love to survive. This weakens our ego and helps subdue our passions. Through this process we are broken down to be fashioned into someone new—someone better. We are given these trials to develop the spiritual stamina that will get us through a lifetime as mothers. This is our chance to *use the struggle to grow in faith and love* as we progress along the path of our own personal salvation.

Even as we struggle, let us take heart and rejoice together in the beauty of motherhood—in the big and small moments filled with a love so deep we don't know where it began, but we are sure it has no end. We must allow ourselves to notice and embrace the many positive and joyful moments: the baby yawns and gurgles, the heavy little body asleep on our chest, the feather-soft tickle of baby hair on our cheek. During these early days, we can lean into these new and simple pleasures even as we let go of some old ones. We can ask the Lord to guide us and let our prayers flow from this raw place as we allow ourselves to experience and be present in this new, precious, and pivotal season of life.

SASHA

In the middle of the first night home with our first child, I hit a breaking point. Our son had woken up for the seventeenth time. We struggled to achieve that same swaddling method our nurses did so effortlessly, the one that our nearly-ten-pounder wouldn't be able to wriggle out of right away. My breasts were feeling ragged and sore from trying to soothe him. My body was so tired, and I felt completely incapable and unprepared.

I looked despairingly into my husband's eyes and said with a humbled earnestness, "I don't think I can do this. I think we may need to have someone adopt him." I was wrecked. My husband looked at me kindly, assured me we could do this, Googled a video on "super swaddles" (involving various layers and folds), and got our little one and me back to sleep.

That was a moment of true awakening—of realizing that life would never be the same. *I* would never be the same. What came before was behind me now, and I needed to open myself to what lay ahead. By the grace of God, after sleep and a bit more breastfeeding coaching, I felt much better.

In a way it feels shameful to admit that those were my honest thoughts, but I have shared that story with many patients and new mothers to let them know they are not alone in their moments of unbelief or hopelessness. God is merciful, and our trials are a *part* of His mercy. A resident of my medical training program, in her graduation speech, quoted Mother Teresa of Calcutta expressing a sentiment that rings true for me especially at moments like this: "I know God will not give me anything I can't handle. I just wish He didn't trust me so much."

For Mind & Body

THE SILVER LINING OF OUR POSTPARTUM STRUGGLE

By day three, you are hopefully settling back into being home. Of course, the road will be different for some. You may be dealing with a baby born prematurely or one who needs a bit more care. Your first night at home with baby may be far off yet, in which case your struggles are uniquely challenging and important in your journey. May the Lord pour forth His grace on all who endure this difficulty!

For those of us who just spent our first night at home with our baby—away from the support of nursing care and expert swaddlers—we may find the first few nights at home very challenging. The deep exhaustion of giving birth sinks in. Our body is actively healing and changing. We are bleeding and swollen, and if we've been breastfeeding, our nipples may be sore. It can be hard to detach from the intensity of pain and discomfort in our bodies.

Many women find that the hormonal shifts, lack of sleep, physical exhaustion, and soreness of birth often come to a peak around now, making for huge emotional swings. This is important to remember when we may feel that the change is too great, the responsibility too much. Childbirth and the care of a newborn are very challenging, both emotionally and physically. One of the best things we can do in these difficult moments is just to be where we are. Acknowledge the pain, soreness, and tiredness.

We can try to accept them as our battle wounds of transformation—a part of the process of receiving the gift of our child and our role as a mother.

For most of us, the intense physical toll of infancy is a passing stage. We can take comfort that it won't always be this way. We became mothers either by the hard work of growing a baby and giving birth or through the long and emotional process of adoption, but our becoming isn't complete. We will face different challenges as our baby grows, and through these we will grow too. We grow in strength so that we will be ready for the tantrums, the boundaries that need drawing, the lessons, and the day-to-day care that raising a child requires. Each phase has blessings and challenges. The way we learn and grow as mothers helps prepare us for the road ahead.

SARAH

I remember when my milk came in for the first time. I was in the shower after returning home from the hospital. My breasts were painful and swollen. My stomach was deflated, and I ached everywhere. I was astonished by the change in my body. I was not prepared for how bruised and sore I was after birth. I let the hot water run over me while I cried and cried. I was deeply joyful inside, but I hurt, and I was so tired and emotionally exhausted from the awesome experience of the previous few days. The intense physical changes were visceral markers for the internal shifts that were beginning. I knew I was growing and changing. The growth hurt—it was both beautiful and completely scary.

DAY 4

Exile

Embracing a New Reality

Exile means that we leave forever everything in our own country that prevents us from reaching the goal of piety.

—SAINT JOHN CLIMACUS[19]

That which a man loves, to which he turns, that he will find. If he loves earthly things, he will find earthly things, and these earthly things will abide in his heart, will communicate their earthliness to him and will find him; if he loves heavenly things, he will find heavenly things, and they will abide in his heart and give him life.

—SAINT JOHN OF KRONSTADT[20]

Do not rivet your eyes to the earth on which you are a momentary actor, on which you are an exile. . . . Use the short

---

19   *Ladder*, p. 14.
20   St. John of Kronstadt, *My Life in Christ* (Jordanville, NY: Holy Trinity Monastery, 1994), p. 69.

spell of your pilgrimage on earth to acquire a haven of peace, a blessed refuge in eternity.

—BISHOP IGNATIUS BRIANCHANINOV[21]

For the Soul

Being home with a new baby brings many feelings: relief, overwhelm, fulfillment, fear, unspeakable joy, sadness, and more. While the world marches on outside our door, a new world is developing before us. As we settle into some sort of rhythm with our baby, we may notice a certain quietness that was not present in our life just a few days ago. Yes, there is crying, but there are also many moments of quietly feeding, rocking, and soothing our baby throughout the day and night. For some this can be a blessing, while for others it can be unnerving. For all of us living in the world, it can seem like a form of exile. While exile isn't typically thought of as a positive state of being, in new motherhood it can bring clarity to our transition and a renewed reliance on God. This time can help us become aware of what we left behind (even if temporarily) as well as what we allow to fill the space that is opening.

We have just been given the gift of another soul. The seeds that we plant in our own lives will affect not just our own salvation but that of our children. As St. John of Kronstadt reminds us above, that which we love, we will find. While our child is probably unaware of anything other than his own bodily needs and our loving presence, he is becoming more and more cognizant of the world around him every day. As we begin our journey, we can think about how we will establish our own "little church" and bring Christ into our home in a lasting and visible way.

---

21 Ignatius Brianchaninov, *The Arena: Guidelines for Spiritual and Monastic Life*, trans. Lazarus Moore (Jordanville, NY: Holy Trinity Monastery, 1982), p. 91.

Day four with a new baby is a good time to set the intention and start small. As we find ourselves with more time and energy, we can do more. For now, choose something easy, such as playing church music for a period each day, speaking with God often, keeping icons in sight of the places you most frequently sit, or choosing a favorite hymn or psalm to sing to your baby as she is falling asleep. While we may feel exiled from the world right now, we are never exiled from God's love.

SASHA

With my first two children, I was too caught up in tending to their basic necessities and keeping the house and my life in some sort of order to consider the spiritual environment I was creating around them. I remember many sleepless nights singing James Taylor's "Sweet Baby James" to my firstborn. By the time my third was born, our family was in a rhythm of prayer that, by the grace of God, we had cultivated. I found myself singing my baby to sleep with the hymn of the Beatitudes from the Divine Liturgy, which begins "In Thy Kingdom remember us, O Lord, when Thou comest in Thy Kingdom." Two years later, I still find myself using this hymn to soothe him. I feel a deep peace within my heart knowing that this hymn and this prayer now lie forever in his subconscious, connected with these moments of his mother's loving presence.

For Mind & Body

BONDING & SELF-ACCEPTANCE

In these first days, we look at the many ways becoming a mother can shift, detach, and separate us from our pre-child life.

However, having a child also opens up a new world of interactions, socializing, and, of course, a relationship with our baby! This developing relationship between our baby and ourselves is referred to as attachment and bonding. It is an important part of our new life with our baby.

Some women instantaneously feel blissfully connected and fiercely protective of their newborns. Other women feel their babies are foreign and have a harder time connecting, or they may feel scared that they don't have the maternal instinct. Whatever we feel in these early days, we must be gentle with ourselves. This experience is brand new with this baby—even if we've had children previously, we've never been in this same place with this new child.

Bonding is a process that takes place over time. Sometimes new mothers are so grateful, and at the same time so fearful of harming or losing their baby, that a strong attachment can take some time and trust to develop. If this is the case, we can remember not to judge ourselves. This is a new relationship that will grow as we get more comfortable with our new role and our baby. During this time we must remember to pray. *Prayer is the way.* Praying to the Theotokos can be particularly helpful at this time. Ask the Theotokos to intercede on your behalf and to fill you with trust in her Son's mercy and love for your child.

⌒

The forty days can feel isolating—with my first child I struggled, because I missed my church family and services so much. I got a blessing to come back early, and I was grateful for that. But with later births I've been really grateful for the peace and quiet and rest the church gives its blessing to during that time. It's a gift to stay home, bond with the new baby, and be blessed with time to pray and be quiet.

—ANNIE, ORTHODOX MOTHER

~

SARAH

With my first daughter, I remember moments of intense fear about her fragility. Would I be able to keep her safe? I remember praying to God, the Theotokos, and our patron saints at random moments throughout the day, for her safety and help with my worry. I wrote this prayer in remembering those early days.

✠ PRAYER FOR NEW MOTHERS ✠

Dear Lord, have mercy on me, Your handmaiden. Thank You for the great gift of my child. I offer You my love and gratitude for entrusting me with the care of this child. I pray that my baby remains healthy in body and mind. I pray You to give me strength to nourish, care for, and guide this child all the days of my life. Aid my healing during this time and keep me healthy so that I may be strong and present for my child. I ask that You have mercy on me in my weakness and relieve my fears. Enter into my soul and cleanse me of my worry. Shine light in the dark spaces and make room for Your love to fill me and shine on my child. Thank you, Lord, for choosing me to be this child's mother. Amen.

PART III

Maternal Virtues

The mother's spiritual life will quietly help her children's souls too. Thus her children will live joyfully and she will be happy too because she has Christ inside her.

—SAINT PAISIOS[1]

1   St. Paisios the Athonite, *Spiritual Counsels 4: Family Life* (Thessaloniki, Greece: Holy Hesychasterion, 2012), p. 95.

DAY 5

Obedience

Surrendering to God's Will

Obedience is the tomb of the will and the resurrection of humility.

—SAINT JOHN CLIMACUS[2]

The grace of the Holy Spirit which is given mystically to every Christian when he is baptized acts and is manifested in proportion to our obedience to the commandments of the Lord. That is, if a Christian obeys the commandments of the Lord more, grace acts with him more, while if he obeys them less, grace acts within him less. Just as a spark, when covered in the ashes of fire becomes increasingly manifest as one removes the ashes, and the more fire wood you put the more the fire burns, so the grace that has been given to every Christian through Holy Baptism is hidden in the heart and covered up by the passions and sins, and the more a man acts

---

2   *Ladder*, pp. 21–23.

in accordance with the commandments of Christ, the more he is cleansed of the passions and the more the fire of Divine grace lights in his heart, illumines and deifies him.

—SAINT NIKODEMOS OF THE HOLY MOUNTAIN[3]

The yoke of Christ is sweet and His burden light unto refreshment for those who submit to it; but all things alien to the teachings of the Gospel are heavy and burdensome.

—SAINT BASIL[4]

For the Soul

Obedience is the first of the virtues on St. John's ladder. We start with obedience here as a foundational building block for the maternal virtues. It was *dis*obedience that provoked the initial Fall of mankind from Paradise, and it follows that obedience will pave our way back home.

The word *obedience* may at first sound outdated or overly traditional. In our modern world, obedience isn't always viewed as a positive attribute, especially for women. We have worked very hard to let our voices be heard; only in the last one hundred and twenty years or so have we gained basic rights such as owning property and voting. As women living in a modern world, we have worked hard to be able to have careers outside the home if we choose. Being told that we need to be obedient can cause some of us to cringe, fearing we must give over our will and rights and

---

3   St. Nikodemos of the Holy Mountain, *Christian Morality* (Belmont, MA: Institute for Byzantine and Modern Greek Studies, 2011).

4   St. Basil the Great, "The Morals" in "Rule 44," *St. Basil: Ascetical Works*, trans. M. Monica Wagner, The Fathers of the Church: A New Translation, vol. 9 (Washington, DC: Catholic University of America Press, 1962), pp. 330–337.

reassume submissiveness. Throughout history and up to the present day, female obedience takes many social and religious forms. It is important to note we are discussing humanity's obedience to God—an obedience that transcends gender and age.

We can take comfort that our obedience is to God and freely given. In his interpretation of *The Ladder of Divine Ascent*, Fr. Papavassiliou writes, "True obedience, like true love, cannot be forced—it must be free."[5] We are free to choose to rise in the morning and turn our day over to His will in prayer. We are free to seek Him. It is our choice. This ultimately brings us freedom as well: "And I will walk at liberty, / For I seek your precepts" (Ps. 119:45). In our Christian understanding of obedience, we freely choose to obey the word of God and humble ourselves to this obedience, understanding this is necessary in order to draw closer to Him.

Being obedient to God involves both internal surrender and external action. Those of us who entered motherhood through childbirth may have experienced such surrender during labor. If we were able to breathe through and release into our contractions, rather than tensing and fighting, we set our body free to do the work and birth our baby. Likewise, in humbling ourselves in obedience to the Lord, we surrender our will to His. We surrender our fight to be in control, allowing Him to guide us and work His grace in us.

Surrender is not passive but active and cannot be forced; it must be cultivated and prayed for. *We start where we are.* We get on our knees, we physically humble ourselves, and we call out to God, saying, "Help me surrender my will to Yours. Help me humble myself before You. Teach me, Lord; show me Your will." And then

---

5   Vassilios Papavassiliou, *Thirty Steps to Heaven: The Ladder of Divine Ascent for All Walks of Life* (Chesterton, IN: Ancient Faith Publishing, 2013), p. 35.

we wait. We listen. We pray. We do this again and again, making space, making room in our hearts and lives to follow God.

Externally, obedience is living the word of God by following His commandments and the example of Jesus. How this looks in each of our lives may be different, and this is where prayer, confession, and following the guidance of a spiritual father are important. Parenting will give us a myriad of opportunities both to practice and to coach obedience.

Obedience to the will of another flows from renunciation of our own will (Day Two), and by today we are well versed in how many of our own desires we have had to put aside to care for our new baby. Each time we pull ourselves from the sweet slumber that perhaps we only just settled into to attend to our child, we are practicing obedience. How many times in our children's lives will we actively choose to put their needs and wants before our own? Every time we practice putting another's will first, we are practicing obedience.

We are God's children, just as this child is ours. In these early days of wonder, we may begin to tap into the depth of love that our children awaken in us. This may give us a glimpse of the boundless love that God has for us. It is in beginning to understand this love that we come to a place of wanting to obey Him. In this way we also hope to inspire our children, through love, to want to obey us—not out of fear but out of love.

～

With my whole heart I have sought You;
Oh, let me not wander from Your commandments!

—PSALM 119:10

～

86

SARAH

My pregnancies were physically challenging (more than the average pregnancy), and I believe this was, in part, to help prepare me for motherhood—to subdue my body and will through suffering. The Lord knew how much I needed to grow in obedience, humility, and patience. My journey of motherhood has held many challenges, and the writing of this book has helped me see even more clearly the beauty of God's mercy.

Being a mother is hard and wonderful. My children are the most joyful thing in my life, yet demand so much of me. Every day I continue to discover just how much my struggle forces me to contend with my passions and face my sinfulness. Through God's mercy, light is finding its way in, and I feel my edges are softening as my heart grows in love. My hope is that as a result of my sharing this awareness, others will know they are not alone in their struggle and will be encouraged to trust in God's love and mercy on their path to salvation.

Saintly Mothers

In the Orthodox tradition, saints are an important part of faithful life. We talk to them in prayer, contemplate their lives, and are bolstered by their steadfast love and commitment to God. Saints give us comfort and solace in our struggle. Many sacrificed their lives, while others spent their days in quiet, pious struggle, ever vigilant to keep their hearts, minds, and bodies devoted to God. There were many saints who were married and many mothers who are examples of spiritual strength, giving us hope and strength on our own journey as we read and reflect on what they endured. After all, though extraordinary people, these saints were human women like ourselves. We all have the capacity to become saintly in our own ways. Throughout the book we offer brief glimpses of saints who were mothers so that we may pray for them to intercede on our behalf along our journey.

☦ SAINT MONICA (MAY 4/17) ☦

North Africa, 332[6]

Monica was a young Christian woman pledged in marriage to a pagan man twice her age and known for his dissolute lifestyle. We can only imagine how she felt on her betrothal. Even though she lived in a very different culture, time, and place from ours, it must have been hard for her to look toward her future marriage to a man who did not share her faith or values. Saint Monica honored her parents' wishes and was married. Though her marriage was very difficult, she remained steadfast in her faith, and after sixteen years her prayers bore fruit when her husband was baptized. During this time she bore three children, one of whom became St. Augustine of Hippo. His return to following the path of God after wandering far into a wayward lifestyle is attributed to the fervent love and prayers of his saintly mother.

Many times in our own lives we may find ourselves in positions we did not wish for, or choices we've made may lead us down a path we didn't anticipate. We look to St. Monica in our struggle as a model of prayerful obedience and faith.

---

6   "St. Monica: Model of Wifely Forbearance," *Orthodox America* no. 154, Vol. 17, No. 6, February, 1998.

For Mind & Body

THE BABY BLUES

It is normal after having a child to feel overwhelmed with love one moment and sad, tired, burdened, and crying the next. This normal part of the postpartum experience is known as the "baby blues" and affects up to eighty percent of women.[7] The combination of hormonal shifts, poor sleep, and for many, a complete shift in day-to-day rhythms and movements leaves many women emotionally volatile and tearful. Even if you did not give birth, sleep deprivation and comparative social isolation can leave you feeling emotionally raw.

As you begin to get more sleep and find some routine, and your postpartum hormones stabilize, these symptoms should begin to resolve. If you feel that your mood is beginning to make it hard for you to care for yourself or your baby, this is when you need to ask for help. This might be noticeable even within the first few weeks. Simply talking with your partner or a support person and getting some additional help around the house or aid in night-time feedings may be enough to help you over the hump. For some, however, it might mean seeking out your healthcare provider. The line between baby blues and more significant postpartum depression can seem hard to define. A healthcare provider you know and trust will be the best person to guide you to the right solutions. While obedience to God does mean acceptance and struggle with our passions and our own demons, we are not called to struggle alone. This period of transition is a time when we need the love and support of others more than ever.

---

7   Katherine L. Wisner, et al., "Onset timing, thoughts of self-harm, and diagnoses in postpartum women with screen-positive depression findings," *JAMA Psychiatry* vol. 70,5 (2013): 490–98.

SASHA

A few weeks after the birth of our first child, I was a mess. Insufficient sleep has always been hard for me to deal with; I remember post-call days during my medical training were often tear filled. The combination of lack of sleep and a complete change in the rhythm of my days (from just finishing a busy medical residency to spending days alone at home with a helpless infant) made for a challenging time. I remember showing up for a two-week follow-up appointment with my midwife in a puddle of tears—my own body still healing, my baby crying. The midwife held my son, looked at me so kindly, and prescribed pumping milk so I could get help with nighttime feeds and joining some new moms groups. I did both, and life became easier and more joy-filled again almost immediately. Glory to God for His mercies!

DAY 6

Repentance

A Change of Heart

Repentance is the renewal of baptism. Repentance is a contract with God for a second life. . . . Repentance is purification of the conscience.

—SAINT JOHN CLIMACUS[8]

Therefore, don't despair when you fall, but get up eagerly and do a metanoia saying, "Forgive me, my dear Christ. I am human and weak." The Lord has not abandoned you. But since you still have a great deal of worldly pride, a great deal of vainglory, our Christ lets you make mistakes and fall, so that you perceive and come to know your weakness every day, so that you become patient with others who make mistakes, and so that you do not judge the brethren when they make mistakes, but rather put up with them.

—ELDER JOSEPH THE HESYCHAST[9]

---

8   *Ladder*, p. 54.
9   From *Elder Joseph the Hesychast: Struggles, Experiences, Teachings*, accessed April 2, 2021, http://www.orthodoxchurchquotes.com/2013/07/20/elder-

If he fights sin and is wounded but continues the struggle,
repents, asks forgiveness and help from God, then he is a holy
soldier of Christ. In this battle with sin he acquires many
spiritual treasures which he could not do otherwise.

—ABBOT NIKON VOROBIEV[10]

For the Soul

As we discussed in DAY 4: EXILE, having a child leads us into a new world. From this place, we may feel differently about certain aspects of our lives and our past actions, and we may begin to gain clarity on how we want to move forward. The precious eyes looking up at us with total trust and endless love can stir a desire in our hearts to be the mother our child needs. Repentance is an important start to this journey.

The Greek word usually translated as "repentance," *metanoia*, literally means "change of heart" or "change of mind" (*meta* = change, *noia* = notion/mind). It is a recognition of the fact that we make mistakes, over and over. In repentance, we humble ourselves, seeing that we have flaws and are not always on the right path, and then we make a change. Rather than a passive sorrow and regret, *metanoia* calls for a more active recognition of the right path—a reorienting toward the Truth.

Father Papavassiliou writes, "Falling and getting up again, starting over—this is what repentance and Christian devotion are all about."[11] This is also what motherhood is like. We are continually being broken down and opened up by love, growing, regrouping, and trying again. As in all aspects of our lives, we are not and

joseph-the-heychest-letter-about-falling-down-and-getting-up/.

10   Abbot Nikon, *Letters to Spiritual Children* (Nikodemos Orthodox Publication Society, 1997), p. 113.

11   *Thirty Steps to Heaven*, p. 15.

never will be perfect. We are fallen. We can only start with this understanding and keep trying, keep asking for mercy, and keep our hearts open to God. *We start where we are.* The fact that we are called upon to repent, not just once but daily, is a blessing. It allows us to recognize that we aren't called to be perfect, but rather continually, moment by moment, to recognize our imperfections and turn back toward God. We make mistakes, we recognize them, and we correct our paths—day after day after day.

SARAH

Over the years, Sasha and I have each called the other after bleak moments of parenting. I remember one such call while I sobbed after dropping my daughters off at school because the morning was rough and I was not loving or patient as I rushed them out the door. Sasha told me it was okay; when they got home I could tell them I loved them and ask for forgiveness. What I could do at that moment was to forgive myself, recognize that I was not a perfect mother, repent of my angry actions, and move forward in love.

➤ PRACTICE ◄

Continuing a Spirit of Confession

We uproot the passions through holy confession. We expose them to the light of God . . . the light will cleanse our hearts and give us peace.

—FATHER SPYRIDON SCHNEIDER[12]

---

12 Fr. Spyridon Schneider, "Sermon 18th Sunday After Pentecost," accessed June 30, 2020, https://stjohntherussian.com/files/Sermons/SermonFS191020.mp3.

In our fallen world, sin is what separates us from God. Repentance is the way we lift our hearts out of sin, and confession is the medicine that heals our souls. Confession is part of our spiritual self-care. A beautiful practice, during these forty days and beyond, is to take note daily of things we have done that separate us from God. Especially during this time, we may find that memories, emotions, fears, and a desire to repent are strong. This is a good time to take brief moments in silence, perhaps with a sleeping baby on our shoulder, to talk to God about these feelings, repent, and pray for strength and commitment to move forward on the right path. It can also be helpful to write down things we want to bring to our confessor when we return to church, to aid our memory when the time to confess again draws near.

For Mind & Body

CHECK-IN

We're sure a lot has happened in the last five days, and moments to yourself may be hard to find. Take a minute to check in with your physical needs. Are you comfortable? Do you need another pillow or perhaps a blanket to cover your feet? Did you drink enough water today? Are you hungry? If someone is there to help, ask for a cup of tea and a snack, possibly some eggs with toast or a piece of fruit with some nuts and cheese. It's important to remember to make time to check in with yourself, to assess what you need and what might make quiet moments a little more comfortable. This is for your comfort, which can feel selfish or self-indulgent sometimes, but it is an important part of self-care and of your family's well-being and comfort as well. *Our peace brings peace.*

Finding Peace in Self-Care

As Christians we know that constantly indulging in our own comfort can pave the way for sin. We see inspiring examples of saints and monastics who are sanctified through denial of their own physical needs. Yet we also know that our bodies and souls are intricately connected and that our physical well-being affects our emotional and spiritual well-being, and vice versa. God knows this too and sometimes gives us physical, emotional, and spiritual challenges to help remind us of our need for Him.

This time is filled with struggle, and we are also granted great *economia*.[13] Our work right now is to care for this tiny life as best we can. Just as it meant during pregnancy and will continue to mean for the rest of our lives as mothers, that means caring for ourselves first.

In Part I (page 42) we included an extensive introduction to self-care in its many forms, from physical and spiritual to finding connection and purpose. Now that you are in the throes of life with a newborn, we encourage you to go back and reread that section. We will continue throughout the book to remind you to care for yourself. There are many ways we will be called to deny ourselves during this time, but being out of touch with what we are needing physically and emotionally is not one of them. It only threatens to lead us away from having the strength and stamina to pursue all things holy. It leads us instead toward discontent, despondency, and despair.

---

13   *Economia* is the adaptation or relaxation of normal church practices or "rules" in order to accommodate an individual's needs.

Remembrance of Death

Each Moment Is Precious

The remembrance of death amongst those in the midst of society gives birth to distress and meditation, and even more, to despondency. But amongst those who are free from noise, it produces the putting aside of cares and constant prayer and guarding of the mind.

—SAINT JOHN OF CLIMACUS[14]

We see the water of a river flowing uninterruptedly and passing away, and all that floats on its surface, rubbish or beams of trees, all pass by. Christian! So does our life. . . . I was an infant, and that time has gone. I was an adolescent, and that too has passed. I was a young man, and that too is far behind me. The strong and mature man that I was is no more. My hair turns white, I succumb to age, but that too passes; I approach the end and will go the way of all flesh. I was born

---

14   *Ladder*, p. 66.

*in order to die. I die that I may live. Remember me, O Lord,
in Thy Kingdom!*

—SAINT TIKHON OF VORONEZH[15]

Forgetful of a physical death, we die a spiritual death.

—BISHOP IGNATIUS BRIANCHANINOV[16]

For the Soul

During this time when we are separated from the hustle and business of daily cares, when we are so close to the miracle of life, we are also faced with the reality of our mortality. While we thank God that we live in a time and place where childbirth is much safer and we have technology to care for babies born prematurely and those who struggle at birth, many of us may have had intense and even scary moments in our labor or early days with our child. This is sobering and prompts us to take a look at our life as a whole. In addition, when we become mothers, the thought of our own death can become even more worrisome as we fear leaving behind our helpless child.

We certainly pray that your health and the health of your child are not in jeopardy in these early days. If you are in the midst of a health crisis—either with a baby born prematurely or with some other problem requiring a bit of extra care—may God keep you and protect you and your child.

Even if our labor and birth were free of such struggles, remembrance of death still remains a crucial part of living in the world as a Christian. In these early days of being a new parent, holding a helpless newborn in our arms, many of us feel this frailty more

---

15 Nadejda Gorodetzky, *St. Tikhon of Zadonsk, Inspirer of Dostoevsky* (Crestwood, NY: St Vladimir's Seminary Press, 1997), pp. 72–74.

16 *Arena*, p. 90.

keenly. Especially if this is our first child, there is a sense of awe and uncertainty in everything: "Is she breathing? What is this rash? How do I hold his head?" If we gave birth in the hospital or birth center, the moment we go home with this tiny life in our keeping we become aware of the awesomeness of our new responsibility. Our own physical well-being takes on a new significance too—we know that we are needed in a vital way.

We may have felt the fragility of life before. Perhaps we lost a loved one or were close to death ourselves. Many of us have lost children through miscarriage or after birth, and we may be holding these memories as we bond with our new baby.[17] Saint John of Climacus writes, "a perfect sense of death is free from fear."[18] For most of us struggling in the world, this is not our experience. Fear permeates our culture in regard to death: fear of pain, fear of losing control, fear of the unknown. Even as Christians we fear the final judgment. At the beginning of our baby's life, how can we understand this sentiment, and how can it help us in these earliest days?

Each day is a gift, and there are no guarantees. Our baby is a gift. The chance to be a mother is a gift, as is waking in the morning and learning how to be a woman raising a child. When we are filled with happiness and contentment holding our child, we remember that this baby is a blessing, and the love we feel is a glimpse of the glory of God. When we are sore, tired, and struggling, we remember that these feelings mean we are alive and our suffering can help us grow. We can remember that we will not always have a body to teach us that we can turn our pain into prayer. When we remember that life ends, that *our* life ends, we can remember that each day is precious.

---

17   Please read our section on miscarriage and loss on page 362.
18   *Ladder*, p. 68.

~

Tears over our departure produce fear. But when fear gives birth to fearlessness, joy dawns. But when constant joy is obtained, holy love bursts into flower.

—SAINT JOHN CLIMACUS[19]

~

This precious gift of life is ours to do with as we please. If we keep in our mind that our ultimate home is with God, how we live will be guided by Him. Remembering to focus on what is truly important will help to ease our daily worries and anxieties. When we measure our everyday concerns against the big picture of our lives and the goal of salvation we have for ourselves and our children, we can begin to lay our cares on God and let Him tend to the bumps in the road.

SASHA

Just before the birth of my first child a friend told me, "Being a parent makes you vulnerable in a way you never could imagine before." Few words of parental wisdom have rung so true for me. What an awesome responsibility it is to be a parent! When I first wrote this reflection, I wrote of a scary five days of high fever I passed with my daughter at age three, when even with my extensive medical training and knowledge I felt helpless. As Sarah and I sit putting the finishing touches on the book, we are in the midst of the coronavirus pandemic, rife with global suffering and uncertainty. Again my medical expertise is not enough. In these moments I am humbled to realize that only God is enough.

---

19   Ibid., p. 78.

As Christians we know that truly all of life is in God's hands. Sitting here as I write, I pray that God will forgive me for my pride in believing that I have power over death and will help me to put my faith in Him—not solely to keep my family physically safe, but more importantly, to provide for us that which we truly need for our eternal salvation.

For Mind & Body

JOURNALING AND WRITING OUR BABY'S BIRTH STORY

Throughout this book we encourage writing in a journal to reflect on the themes we discuss during this period of transition and growth. Research suggests that journaling can be beneficial for both your emotional and physical health.[20] We invite you to think of your journal as part of your self-care and not as another to-do.

This journal is just for you. It is a place to externalize the many new and sometimes worrisome thoughts that are whirling around in your mind. It can also be a place to notice the good and the small unsung joys that exist in this time. Throughout our forty days together, we will encourage intentional time for gratitude, and this journal can be a place to record that also.

Sometimes just writing and letting the words flow can help us to understand things that we have been thinking and feeling of which we were not fully aware. While the depth of what we share in journals can seem quite personal, we can also imagine it becoming a treasure for our children, perhaps when they are in the first days with their children, God willing, or even after our

---

20 J. W. Pennebaker, "Writing about emotional experiences as a therapeutic process," *Psychological Science*, 8(3) 162–166, 1997; and M. Purcell, "The Health Benefits of Journaling," Psych Central, accessed July 3, 2020, https://psychcentral.com/lib/the-health-benefits-of-journaling/.

repose. However, this is completely optional. The main point is to remain connected with the murmurings of our own hearts and minds so that we can be aware of where we are struggling and how best to move forward.

➤ EXERCISE ◄

Writing Our Baby's Birth Story

Congratulations on having a week-old baby! While it is still fresh in your mind, take a few minutes to capture the events, feelings, and precious moments of your baby's birth. Take note of how you went into labor, your feelings, who was with you, and your reflection on the birth process. Share about the experience of meeting your baby. If you adopted your child, spend a few moments capturing those first moments of meeting your child and the day your child became yours to keep.

Many of us have birth experiences that were very different from what we expected. Some of us may even feel that our child's birth was traumatic and that our voice was stifled during the birth process. We may be left feeling vulnerable, belittled, hurt, or as if we have failed. If your birth was very different from what you expected or if you have painful feelings around the birth, this is a good place to start processing those feelings. Writing them down will help you share them as you feel able. If your experience was a positive one and left you feeling strong, confident, and filled with joy, write this down too. Having a written record and a chance to review and remember this life-changing event is a gift to yourself.

Naming

What's in a Name?

And when eight days were completed for the circumcision of the Child, His name was called JESUS, the name given by the angel before He was conceived in the womb.

—LUKE 2:21

✠ PRAYERS AT THE NAMING OF A CHILD ✠
ON THE EIGHTH DAY AFTER BIRTH[21]

O Lord our God, we entreat Thee, and we supplicate Thee, that the light of Thy countenance be signed on this, Thy servant (handmaid), N., and that the Cross of Thine Only-begotten Son be signed in his (her) heart and understanding, so that he (she) may flee from the vanity of the world and from every evil snare of the enemy, and may follow after Thy commandments. And grant, O Lord, that Thy holy name may remain unrejected by him (her), and that, in

---

21 *Holy Needs,* pp. 7–9.

due time, he (she) may be joined to Thy Holy Church, and that he (she) may be perfected by the dread Mysteries of Thy Christ, so that, having lived according to Thy commandments, and having preserved the seal unbroken, he (she) may receive the blessedness of the Elect in Thy Kingdom. By the grace and love for mankind of Thine Only-begotten Son, with Whom Thou art blessed, together with Thy Mostholy, Good and Life Giving Spirit, now and ever, and unto the ages of ages. Amen.

For the Soul

Today is the day that our Orthodox tradition has laid aside for the naming of a new child. Nowadays, many families will have decided on a name or at least a short list of possibilities before the birth of their child. Most of us in the US are required to submit our birth certificate information right away. Unless we leave the name as "baby boy" or "baby girl," we have likely named our child. However, today is the first time the baby's name is formally used by our priest. While both baby and mother are blessed and prayed for on the first day, today our child is recognized as a unique soul, distinct in all of history.

In a baby's initial and slow entrance into the life of the Church, the naming prayers are the second set of formal prayers offered to us. We know there is a lot of variation in how, when, and if these prayers are said. Some women have them done early with the birth prayers, some on the eighth day, some a little later, and some not at all. One mother we spoke to had them said over the phone during a snowstorm!

Despite variations, we find this ancient custom of the eighth-day naming both beautiful and symbolic. Jesus was named on the eighth day, and we do so in imitation of Him. In addition, our temporal world has seven days in a week, and some refer to the eighth day as representing the Kingdom of God, the realm beyond our present time and space. The symbolism of naming on the eighth day brings into focus the fact that the Church is calling our child to life eternal.

A rich history and tradition surrounds the choosing of a name in the Orthodox Church. Early Christians decided to take the names of saints when they were baptized, and this tradition continues today. In some customs, godparents assist in the naming of the child, or a family patron saint's name is given. It is common in Russian practice to name the child for a saint commemorated on or close to the child's birthday.

Having a saint's name is a beautiful connection to the life of the Church for our child and initiates a relationship with a patron saint. Giving our child a saint's name is a reminder to ourselves and to all who say and hear the name of holiness, faith, and virtue. We hope our child will strive to follow the example of her namesake saint. This name is used not only on the day of baptism, but it is the name the priest will use to pray for our child and to offer all sacraments, including Holy Communion.

What an amazing privilege and responsibility we have in choosing a name for our child by which he will be known in the world. A name helps to shape an identity, and we hold the power of this gift in our choice. If you later question your name choice or feel a pull toward a saint other than one who shares your child's given name, you still have a month or so until baptism to change it.

Whether we are able to have the prayers said or not, we can use this day to reflect on how we hope our choice will shape our child's spiritual life and development.

SASHA

My husband and I debated names a lot before the birth of our first child. The name we decided on as a second name was special to my husband as it was his grandfather's name, and he wanted it to be our son's baptismal name. My husband had recently converted to Orthodoxy, and I wanted him to feel deeply connected with the spiritual decisions we were making as we started a family together. However, I also worried about our child's day-to-day name being different from that of his patron saint. At the time, I wasn't really aware of how big a part of my son's life in the Church the name we chose would become.

In the end we came to a compromise. We use our children's first names as their Christian names within the Church, but created a tradition in our family of celebrating both first and second names as saints' names. The children each have two saints' icons by their beds, and we celebrate (at home) both of the saints' days for each child. However, I am extremely thankful that the children take communion with the same name they are called by our friends and neighbors. For me, I came to realize, it was important that my children saw themselves as the same child of God, whether they are in line for communion or for an ice cream at the park.

➤ JOURNALING ◄

Getting to Know Our Patron Saint

When we are baptized into the Orthodox Faith, we are given the name of a patron saint that connects us with a person of flesh and blood, like ourselves, who was victorious in the spiritual battle. Those of us who were baptized as infants did not take part in choosing our patron saint. Many of us who converted as adults may have had our patron saints given by our priests, or perhaps it became clear our patron saint was choosing us.

However we found our way to our namesake, establishing and strengthening the connection to our patron saint is important. Saints give us virtuous examples to strive toward as well as an opportunity for a personal relationship with a warrior of our Faith. Through this connection our saint can become a beacon of hope and an intercessor from whom we can request help. Even some of us born and raised in the Orthodox Church may not be so familiar with our patron. If you are already well connected with your patron saint, what a blessing! Feel free to use the activity below to connect yourself more closely with the saint you have chosen for your child. We offer this practice to be completed however you wish—perhaps as a letter to your patron saint or your own reflections on your understanding of their role in your life. A helpful place to begin is to briefly research and write down the answers to a few of these questions.

» Who is your patron saint?

» What names did your saint go by in life, and how is the saint known after death?

» Why is this person your patron?

» Was the saint chosen for you? Did you pick your saint when you converted? Did anyone else in the family have the same name?

» What was the story of your saint's life?

» When do we celebrate your saint's feast day?

» Consider adding this date to your calendar.

» What troparion is sung in your saint's honor?

» What main qualities of this saint would you like to carry with you and cultivate in your life?

» How can you pray to your saint?

A nice exercise is to think of a quick, sentence-long prayer you can use to connect with your saint quickly (for example, *O holy and God-pleasing Saint Alexandra, pray for me and guide me that I might raise my children to hold tightly to our Faith.*)

After journaling, see if you can find a way to keep the saint's example as a part of your daily life. Do you have an icon of your saint? Is it in sight daily? If not, you can print an image out now and plan to obtain an icon. Try to keep the image of this holy person visible at your desk, by your bed, or in your icon corner. Know that this saint is a guide for you and an intercessor, both in this life and the next.

For Mind & Body

BREASTFEEDING CHECK-IN

As we mentioned in Part I, if you are breastfeeding it is important to offer your baby your breast as often as he is hungry. By day five most women's milk supply will be coming in. By this point you may find that your baby has a good latch and is happy to nurse much of the day, or you may still be struggling quite a bit. It is normal for your nipples to be sore with so much new activity. Take time to position and reposition your baby in these early days in order to create a good latch and prevent additional soreness later on. While lanolin and even breast milk can be soothing to the nipples, we like coconut oil, which has some antiseptic properties and is safe for your baby to ingest. It doubles as an excellent diaper ointment and skin cream when needed. If you find you have sharp pain, pinching, or blisters, get help from a nurse or lactation consultant.

SARAH

When my first daughter was born, I was relieved that she latched quickly. I thought everything was going well when a nurse came in and shook her head. "No, that's not quite right," she said to me in German. She reached over, gently opened my daughter's mouth, took the majority of my breast with her other hand, and put it fully into my daughter's open mouth. "N'ya, that is how she will get milk." I was a bit shocked, but she was right. It felt entirely different and helped my milk production.

By the time I had my third daughter, I was an experienced breast-feeder. Although she seemed to latch well, I felt sharp needles every time she nursed. I thought it was just the newness, but I was relieved when the hospital pediatrician noticed that her tongue tie might be causing trouble. Two days later she had a frenectomy, and after that she fed much better.

DAY 9

Mourning

Our Longing for God

*Mourning according to God is sadness of soul and the dispo-
sition of a sorrowing heart, which ever madly seeks that for
which it thirsts; and when it fails in its quest, it painfully pursues it, and follows in its wake grievously lamenting.*

—SAINT JOHN CLIMACUS[22]

*So weep, shed streams of tears, and soften the earth of your
heart. Once the ground is wet, you can easily uproot the thorns.*

—ELDER JOSEPH THE HESYCHAST[23]

*O most holy Virgin, hearken unto the voice of thine unprofit-
able servant. Grant me torrents of tears, O most pure one, to
cleanse my soul from impurity.*

—PRAYER VII TO THE MOST HOLY THEOTOKOS[24]

---

22 *Ladder*, p. 70.
23 Elder Joseph the Hesychast, "Letter."
24 Holy Trinity Monastery, *Prayer Book* (Jordanville, NY: Holy Trinity Monas-
    tery), p. 22.

For the Soul

In his Sermon on the Mount, Jesus gave us the path to God by sharing the Beatitudes. The second of these is "Blessed *are* those who mourn, / For they shall be comforted" (Matt. 5:4). From our Savior's mouth we learn that mourning is a blessed state, and in it we will be comforted. This can be hard to take in. We may wonder, why must we mourn to be with God?

To grasp why our loving God would bless a state of mourning, we need to contemplate what it is we are mourning. Spiritual mourning is different from our secular perception of sadness and grief. In our spiritual lives, mourning is an awareness that we live in a fallen world. In this place, where we have free will to act and be however we wish, we experience separation from God. We long for Him, and in our longing we feel the sadness of separation and mourn that we cannot be with Him.

From this deep place in our soul, we feel the distance, and we search for *something* to fill our emptiness—from life-affirming options, such as family, community, and meaningful work, to destructive ones, such as power, worldly praise, alcohol or drugs, and endless distraction. We may enjoy these attempts for a while, but they will not satisfy. Archimandrite Seraphim Aleksiev, in his guide to repentance, calls this our "blessed hunger" for God. He goes on to describe God as the "paramount bliss for which our heart is constantly yearning."[25]

In becoming mothers, we pass through a certain phase of mourning. Our mourning as mothers is different from the spiritual mourning of being separated from God. While we have gained so much in becoming mothers, we also recognize that the start of something new often means letting go of what we've

---

25   Archimandrite Seraphim Aleksiev, *The Forgotten Medicine: The Mystery of Repentance* (Wildwood, CA: St. Xenia Skete Press, 1994), p. 17.

had. Many things we took for granted in our pre-child lives will change. We cannot simply walk out the door and go wherever we want, whenever we want. In fact, the simple act of getting out the door has become absurdly difficult. We may be mourning the loss of our livelihood, whether temporary or more permanent. We may mourn the lack of one-on-one time with our partner or older children. Each new season of life brings with it both new wonders and fresh losses. In this light, we can see how in these early days we may mourn some changes and how this may serve our growth as we reach toward God in our struggle.

These forty days are an incredible gift—a time of metamorphosis when we may begin the process of letting go of who we were to make space for who we are becoming. We can use this gift of mourning to mature from our selfishness and grow in compassion, humility, patience, and internal strength, so that we can hold and guide our children with love during even the most trying stages.

Giving ourselves time to reflect and process can help to settle some of the difficult emotions swirling around inside. Becoming a mother adds to our identity as a woman, but the reality of motherhood is often different from what we previously imagined. Allowing ourselves time to integrate expectations and reality can help us to move forward in peace. Talking to our partners, close friends, and other mothers can help us to do this. Journaling can play a helpful role in processing and releasing some of these emotions as well as serving to capture memories of these early days.

➤ JOURNALING ◄

Reflecting As We Grow

In this exercise, explore in what ways you are mourning the loss of your old life and making space for the person you are becoming. Reflection questions for your journal:

» What, if anything, are you mourning?

» What do you feel you are letting go of as you become a mother?

» What losses feel celebratory to you?

» What did you expect your early days as a mother to be like?

» How is the reality the same as and/or different from your current experience?

» What are you gaining in your new role?

» What is most difficult for you right now?

» What is your favorite aspect of being a mother so far?

» What parts of your pre-baby self do you want to make sure to bring into your new reality and nurture?

» What new joys, strengths, and aspects of yourself are you discovering in motherhood?

For Mind & Body

MODERN MOTHER MALAISE

For centuries the care of children and home was a woman's domain. Many women found their joy and peace in raising a family while at times also feeling stifled by society's expectations. In our modern culture women can "have it all." We can have careers, marry or not, become mothers or not. We are shown images of busy and successful career moms juggling a work call while making dinner, or of serenely put-together stay-at-home moms happily spending the whole day playing with their children and reading magazines. These ideas of what motherhood is today can lay the foundation for unrealistic expectations.

We need to be careful of internalizing these images and be aware of how they influence our ideas of motherhood. We are in a new era where women want, can, and try to do everything. Many women get married and have children later in life, after education, work, and travel. As many mothers have more life experience prior to having children, it can be hard to give up aspects of their exciting life for the mundane tasks of caring for home and children. On the other hand, those who have children when they are young can feel they are missing out or won't be able to accomplish career goals. This can make the transition to motherhood more difficult.

One way to help the growing pains is to recalibrate our expectations to more fully understand our role as mothers and its purpose in our lives. As we discuss throughout the book, motherhood is one of the ways we can work out our salvation. If we can shift our thinking to see the sacrifices as choices made in love, and the day-to-day struggle as working toward spiritual growth, it can help us to see our own agency in the process.

In Ecclesiastes 3:1 we read, "To everything *there* is a season, / A time to every purpose under heaven." While we will one day miss these early days with a warm bundle in our arms, in times of struggle we can take comfort in knowing that mothering infants and young children is just one season of life. Our children will always need us, while they are living in our homes and beyond. Some say their need is even greater as teenagers than as toddlers. But they won't always need us in the same way, and they certainly won't always be as physically dependent on us as they are now.[26]

---

26 For those whose children have special needs, this may not be the case. Their motherhood has its unique challenges and blessings. *Of Such Is the Kingdom* by Summer Kinard (Ancient Faith Publishing, 2019) is a beautiful

The development of our spiritual life through the bodily exertion of these early days prepares us for the deeper levels of intellectual, emotional, and spiritual strength needed to guide and parent a precocious four-year-old, rebellious teenager, or fearless young adult.

SARAH

Becoming a mother was the fulfillment of a dream for me. Even so, I wasn't prepared for many of the difficulties I encountered. One of the hardest aspects of new motherhood was my inability to be productive. I was used to getting things done. When I had my daughter I felt like my hands were always tied. It was a long, slow ego death for me. I did not take the time as a gift. I was frustrated and wanted to be able to do what I had done before. This was not good for me or my daughter. We both suffered. It took me years (and I still have to pray and consciously be where I am) to let things go and embrace what I can do in the moments I have.

Being present with my children is a gift, and I feel able to accept this gift by acknowledging it as my choice and not regretting everything else I could be doing. I like the saying "You can have it all, but not all at once." This helps me to give thanks to the Lord for the blessing of this time with my children and quells my feelings of being left out as a stay-at-home mom of young kids.

---

book that looks at spiritual life in the context of special needs.

Meekness

Our Peace Brings Peace

Meekness is an unchangeable state of mind, which remains the same in honour and dishonour. . . . Meekness is the rock overlooking the sea of anger, which breaks all the waves that dash against it, yet remains completely unmoved. Meekness is the buttress of patience, the door, or rather the mother of love, and the foundation of discernment.

—SAINT JOHN CLIMACUS[27]

Let them push you, but do not push; let them crucify you, but do not crucify. Let them insult, but do not insult. Let them slander, but do not slander. Be meek, and do not be zealous in evil.

—SAINT ISAAC THE SYRIAN[28]

---

27 *Ladder*, p. 145.
28 Homily 89, *Ascetical Homilies*.

Blessed are the meek, / For they shall inherit the earth.
—THIRD BEATITUDE, MATTHEW 5:5

For the Soul

In our modern-day culture, meekness is often equated with weakness. Merriam-Webster defines meek as "submissive: deficient in spirit and courage" as well as "not violent or strong."[29] In pursuing meekness we can again begin to fear, as we may have with the concept of obedience, that we will lose the strength and influence that we as women have been working to gain over the last centuries. Yet if we look more closely, we see that meekness as a spiritual concept doesn't mean being a pushover. In Matthew 11:29 (KJV) we hear Jesus' admonition, "Take my yoke upon you, and learn of me; for I am meek and lowly in heart: and you shall find rest unto your souls." Jesus, our ultimate example for all the virtues, was meek and humble, yet still an incredibly powerful and influential person.

Spiritually speaking, meekness simply embodies the way a Christian should be in the world. The term *meek* often appears interchangeable with the concept of being "good" in a general sense—kind, patient, compassionate, obedient. Meekness encompasses all the steps we have worked on up until now and all the steps that come after. As such, it is an exceptionally powerful concept and an aspirational virtue.

Saint John's imagery of a meek person being like the rock unflustered by the crashing waves is powerful. Already in this first week with a new baby, we have surely had many moments when it seemed everything was happening at once—the baby

---

29   "Meek," Merriam-Wesbster.com, accessed May 1, 2020, https://www.merri-am-webster.com/dictionary/meek?utm_campaign=sd&utm_medium=serp&utm_source=jsonld.

crying, the phone ringing, something burning on the stove, and so forth. If we have other children, inevitably they will have needs at the same time. These moments are so challenging. How do we keep our cool? How do we remain patient? How can we stay present and full of love even as we feel stretched so thin?

We will do well to remember this image of the rock and to ask God, as St. Tikhon suggests, to grant us the spirit of love and meekness. When we forget to turn to God in the moment, or the temptation to yield to anger overpowers us and we lose our temper, we can ask forgiveness of God and others. We can humble ourselves and recommit to taming our tumultuous souls so that our hearts can truly be a place where the Lord finds rest.

For Mind & Body

MAINTAINING CALM

It can be especially hard to maintain meekness in those moments when everything feels completely chaotic and spiraling out of control. During these times, it can be useful to get into the habit of pausing. Pausing can seem outrageous when things are out of control. After all, it feels as if everything is in a state of emergency—or is it?

Dr. Laura Markham, a clinical psychologist and parenting coach, writes and teaches on the concept of "peaceful parenting."[30] We find her approach very helpful. Much of her work focuses on helping us to manage ourselves and our own emotions so we can be the parents we want to be. It is unpleasant enough when our children are crying or throwing a tantrum, but adding our own tantrum can make things infinitely worse. She suggests that most of the time, these moments that push us to our limits

---

30   Find more information at www.ahaparenting.com.

are not, in fact, emergencies. Our brains may register them as such, but we do well to remember that spilt milk, crying, a diaper explosion, or burnt soup are not true emergencies. If we realize what is happening to us in these moments, we can allow ourselves time to stop, take a breath, and choose love, choose meekness, choose not to act out in anger. Instead, we can turn to God.

⌇

If our thoughts are kind, peaceful, and quiet, turned only toward good, then we also influence ourselves and radiate peace all around us—in our family, in the whole country everywhere. This is true not only here on earth, but in the cosmos as well. When we labor in the fields of the Lord, we create harmony. Divine harmony, peace, and quiet spread everywhere.

—ELDER THADDEUS OF VITOVNICA[31]

⌇

➤ PRACTICE ◀

Making the Sign of the Cross

In her books and blog, Dr. Markham suggests many helpful ways in which we can regulate our feelings and calm our bodies. We wish to add to her ideas our first golden rule of motherhood: *Prayer is the way.* Prayer, as we discuss over and over, can take many different forms. Outward manifestations of prayer such as bowing our heads or making the sign of the cross can sometimes be all we need or are capable of in a stressful moment.

---

31   Elder Thaddeus of Vitovnica, *Our Thoughts Determine Our Lives: The Life and Teachings of Elder Thaddeus of Vitovnica* (Platina, CA: Saint Herman of Alaska Brotherhood, 2009), p. 63.

When temptations are stirred up, the sign of the cross is a powerful weapon. Saint Anthony the Great reminds us, "For they [the demons] are nothing and quickly disappear, especially if a man fortify himself beforehand with faith and the sign of the cross."[32] In a moment when we notice our stress level seems to be at a breaking point, or preferably before that moment arrives, we can try to remember to practice meekness and recognize our own weak and fallen state by simply pausing, bowing our heads, and making the sign of the cross. With time, as our child(ren) grow(s), our practice will begin to leave the lasting impression on them that when the going gets tough, they can simply and quietly turn to God.

---

32 St. Athanasius, *The Life of Saint Anthony the Great* (Virgin Mary of Australia and Oceana, 2019), pp. 20–21.

Patience

Weathering the Storm

Do not be surprised that you fall every day; do not give up, but stand your ground courageously. And assuredly, the angel who guards you will honour your patience.

—SAINT JOHN CLIMACUS[33]

It is God, Who is merciful and grants everyone what he needs, Who is building him up when He gives him more than he needs; in doing so He shows the abundance of His love for men and teaches him to give thanks. When He does not grant him what he needs, He makes him compensate for the thing he needs through the working of the mind and teaches him patience.

—SAINT DOROTHEOS OF GAZA[34]

---

33 *Ladder*, p. 64.
34 St. Dorotheos of Gaza, *Discourses and Sayings*, http://www.orthodox-churchquotes.com/tag/patience/page/2/ (accessed October 22, 2020).

*We must give thanks for all things to the Lord, Who has
rightly given us difficulties that we may learn patience, which
is more beneficial than comforts, and ennobles the soul.*

—SAINT MOSES[35]

For the Soul

Patience may be the step on the ladder that being a mother
most trains and cultivates in us if we let it. Motherhood
requires an incredible amount of patience, and loving patience is
one of the greatest gifts we can give to our children. Saint Nikon
of Optina describes patience as "continuous good humor."[36] With
this definition in mind, we see that patience is our ability to
remain steady, and even joyful, in trying moments. When we are
truly patient, we practice and nurture many other virtues—love,
humility, meekness, obedience. When situations test us, we can
call on the Lord in our hearts and keep our internal state from
flaring up, remaining in good humor. This is a gift to ourselves
and our children: *Our peace brings peace.*

Cultivating our ability to remain patient both gives our children a peaceful environment in which to grow and models for
them how to handle difficulty. Many challenges will come our
way throughout the course of motherhood. The words of the
well-known Serenity Prayer remind us that we cannot change all
things, and those that cannot be changed require our acceptance.
When we truly trust that "all things work together for good to
those who love God" (Rom. 8:28), we can begin to *allow* things
in our lives—whether desired or not—and *accept* our circumstances with faith that we are being given what we need for our

---

35 *Living without Hypocrisy: Spiritual Counsels of the Holy Elders of Optina*
   (Jordanville, NY: Holy Trinity Publications, 2005), p. 4.
36 Ibid., p.192.

own salvation. Many times, we can't see the larger picture or understand how God is working in our lives. This acceptance doesn't mean we don't still work to solve problems or to improve ourselves and grow in Christ. Rather, acceptance allows us to see things as they are and to move forward with patience.

As parents we will make many mistakes. Even with our first child, by day eleven we have already made more than a handful. In fact, while as a culture we don't like to admit it, we make many mistakes each day. Especially for parents, where the stakes feel so high, the fact that we get things wrong over and over again requires us to be extremely patient with ourselves—forgiving ourselves each time we fall and picking ourselves up again, ready to begin anew on our path.

While we often jump to this idea of patiently bearing trials, we should also keep in our mind that patience can be understood as allowing for the natural unfolding of experience. It is a frequent saying in parenthood, "The days are long but the years are short." This can feel most palpably true in the first weeks of motherhood when, as we discussed in DAY 4: EXILE, the rhythm of our lives seems to have come to a grinding halt. It can be so tempting to want to get past this part—to the fun part. We want to rush ahead: *When will she be able to hold her head up? When will he sleep through the night? When will this all get easier?* Here too, patience will benefit us twofold—both in the strengthening of our patience in general and in the acceptance of each moment as a gift from God to be savored and lived, in all its beauty and difficulty.

SASHA

As I mentioned before, I struggled tremendously with the birth of my first child and the transition to being a parent.

The early days were so hard, and I remember desperately asking friends if it gets easier. Many friends, especially those with more than one child, said, "No, this is the easy part." I remember feeling some true despair and being unsure I would be capable of what lay ahead.

After my second and third children were born, I did see that the early days with a new baby seemed easier—but only because I had lived through that phase before. Having lived it before, I can appreciate the little details more since I am not so overwhelmed by the process. So I often do say to my new-mom patients, "Yes, it gets easier," "Yes, this too shall pass."

As I look at my oldest, now so big and becoming his own person, I can feel how quickly these moments pass. I wish sometimes that time would stand still or even go back. What a beautiful thing to live this moment in which we live rather than dwelling always in the past or the future. God, grant me to be present in my life in the here and now that You have laid before me.

➤ PRACTICE ◄

Arrow Prayers

In moments when our good humor threatens to fail and our patience is waning, we can invite God's grace into our lives through prayer. Often the moments when we most need to pray are the very moments when we seem least able to take ourselves out of the world and into our own hearts. Yet prayer need not be complicated or long-winded. Keeping a short prayer in our mind to call on whenever we need strength or encouragement can be a powerful practice. Most of us are already familiar with the Jesus Prayer and its place in unceasing prayer, but there are many prayers and psalms we can repeat in moments of need. All we need to do is to find one that speaks to us. The Orthodox Church has many short prayers—"arrow prayers," as they are sometimes known. Abbot Tryphon of All-Merciful Saviour Monastery on Vashon Island, Washington, writes about these prayers:

Many Church Fathers taught the use of the "arrow prayer," deliberately short prayers for personal devotion that were easily remembered, and could communicate one's love for God, while seeking His help. They were like arrows being shot into the air, wholeheartedly demonstrating our sincerity in asking God's help.[37]

There are many such prayers. Below are a few offerings we find helpful:

» "Create in me a clean heart, O God, and renew a right spirit within me." (Psalm 50:12 OSB)

» "Let God arise and let His enemies be scattered." (Psalm 67:1) *(This is especially to be said while making the sign of the cross.)*

» "Lord, teach me to do Your will."

» "Lord, enlighten my darkness."

» "O Holy God-pleaser *(patron saint's name)*, intercede on our behalf."

» "The Lord watches over my coming out and my going in

---

37   Abbot Tryphon, "Arrow Prayers," *The Morning Offering* (blog), February 9, 2014, https://blogs.ancientfaith.com/morningoffering/2014/02/arrow-prayers-snow-for-sunday-morning/.

both now and forevermore." (Psalm 121:8, paraphrased)

» "Raise my children, O Lady, to be made worthy of the Kingdom of Heaven."[38]

» "Make haste, O God, to deliver me! Make haste to help me, O Lord!" (Psalm 70:1).

» "Yea, though I walk through the valley of the shadow of death, I will fear no evil; For You *are* with me; Your rod and Your staff, they comfort me" (Psalm 23:4).

» "The Lord is my strength and my shield." (Psalm 28:7)

» "Lord, open to me Your mysteries."

» "O Lord, grant me to greet the coming day in peace."

For Mind & Body

TOP BABY CONCERNS

Nearly two weeks into your baby's life, you are hopefully developing some basic rhythms. Many things are still unknown and to be discovered. Especially if this is your first child, you likely have many questions about the practical care of your baby. As a family doctor, Sasha feels these are among the top areas of concern she gets asked about at her patients' two-week well-child checks. We also include a list of our favorite resources at the back of the book.

Baby skin care basics

Our babies have spent their last nine to ten months in a sac of liquid, and being exposed to air can be extremely drying. Although it may seem counterintuitive, we recommend against using soap.

---

38   *Akathist to the Mother of God, Nurturer of Children.*

Soap dries the skin and is the number one reason we see rashes and eczema in newborn babies. We recommend only water baths for at least the first year and natural oils such as coconut oil or jojoba oil for moisturizing and diaper-area care.

Soothing fussy babies

Often these first three months are referred to as the fourth trimester—a time of significant development when babies might be best cared for in the quiet of the womb, but they would be too big to birth at twelve months' gestation. Babies' temperaments vary widely, but for fussier babies, mimicking the womb by using shushing/white noise and swaddles can be very effective. See the five S's of the *Happiest Baby on the Block* book for more ideas. Sometimes all the five methods are needed at once.

How much babies eat

One of the things we worry most about with our children is how much they are eating and whether it is enough. This is especially true with newborns. If we are breastfeeding we may worry we aren't producing enough, and when we bottle-feed we worry about following exact guidelines. In general, God designed our babies to know how much they need. They will cry if they don't get enough and spit up if they get too much. Follow your baby's lead and follow up with your baby's doctor for regularly scheduled weight checks.

Spitting up & gassiness

Lots of people have heard of the term *colic*, which traditionally is used to describe belly pain, often caused by gas, that comes and goes. Nowadays the term is used loosely to describe babies who cry more than expected. This crying is not necessarily related to belly pain, but the term can be confusing to parents. This is a big subject. For now, know that all babies have a little bit of acid reflux due to their physiology. Babies' stomach sphincters are not fully developed, and they can easily slosh food back upward, especially if they haven't burped enough or are laid flat right away. Rarely does a baby need to be treated for reflux—usually only if they are not gaining weight. For crying, see "Soothing fussy babies" above. Some babies need more time upright. "Baby-wearing" can be a great way to help with this.

Tummy time & baby exercises

Since the advent of "back is best" sleeping, babies spend exorbitant amounts of time on their backs. This can mean they don't strengthen their back and neck muscles as quickly, and they can develop flat spots on their heads. These flat spots are normally reversible, but it can help the bones of the head to fuse together symmetrically if we make sure babies get a little bit of tummy time each day. It can be as simple as placing baby belly-down on your chest and trying to make eye contact with her.

Safe sleeping

The medical community strongly recommends putting baby to sleep on his back in a separate crib, without any blankets or toys, to most effectively prevent sudden infant death syndrome (SIDS). As parents we will make our own decisions on many things, and some parents choose not to follow this advice. While we still recommend it as the safest way to sleep, we discuss ways to minimize risk for parents who decide to co-sleep. There are many sleep arrangements that can allow for the sense of co-sleeping. If you decide to co-sleep despite the risks, make sure the mattress is firm and there is no bedding near baby. We recommend making sure only mother and baby are in the bed. Finally, mothers should avoid any alcohol or sedating medications that could impair awareness of where baby is in the bed.

Taking baby out

Babies' immune systems are immature and most vulnerable before six weeks of age. However, that doesn't mean you can't take them out of the house. When they are very small it is important to keep them with you, either in a cloth baby carrier on your body or bundled up in their car seat. If taking baby out, get comfortable asking friends, family, and well-meaning strangers to wash their hands before touching baby. Note: We finish the writing of this book during the coronavirus pandemic, and airborne illnesses like this one slightly change our counseling. If airborne illnesses are of concern, keeping baby out of enclosed spaces with groups of people may be recommended for up to one year.

When to call the doctor

Most importantly, parents want to know when they should call the doctor. First, know that no doctor's office will fault you for calling with a "silly" question, so if your gut says there is something wrong, feel free to call. However, the main things to watch for that would potentially concern a medical professional and require evaluation are:

1. *A rectal temperature above 100.4° F (38° C).* Only a rectal temperature is truly accurate in small babies, so be sure you have a digital thermometer and know how to use it.

2. *Not making wet diapers.* Babies can become dehydrated easily. Watching wet diapers can help us know they are hydrated. If you are with baby, you will have a sense of whether she goes many hours without a wet diaper, but when someone else is

caring for baby, it can be useful to make sure they let you know how many wet diapers they changed.

3. *Lethargy.* People use this term loosely all the time, but true lethargy is when baby is really hard to wake up over a period of time (not just once or twice) or consistently won't wake for feedings for periods of time during the day or at night. This can also be a sign of dehydration and merits evaluation.

4. *Breathing troubles.* This is hard for most new parents (or even seasoned ones) to assess. Babies can make lots of noise when they sleep or have noisy breathing. However, if you notice baby pulling away from feedings frequently to breathe, or a blue tinge around the mouth, or breath-holding episodes, you need to bring baby to be seen right away. This can happen in healthy infants but always requires evaluation and observation by a medical professional.

Any of these symptoms merits a call to your health care provider and likely a visit. However, anything that makes you worried, whether on this list or not, can and should prompt a call to your provider's office.

DAY 12

Thanksgiving

Glory to God for All Things

O come, let us sing unto the Lord: let us make a joyful noise to the rock of our salvation. Let us come before his presence with thanksgiving, and make a joyful noise unto him with psalms. For the Lord is a great God, and a great King above all gods.

—PSALM 95:1–3 (KJV)

When you sit down to eat, pray. When you eat bread, do so thanking Him for being so generous to you. If you drink wine, be mindful of Him who has given it to you for your pleasure and as a relief in sickness. When you dress, thank Him for His kindness in providing you with clothes. When you look at the sky and the beauty of the stars, throw yourself at God's feet and adore Him who in His wisdom has arranged things in this way. Similarly, when the sun goes down and when it rises, when you are asleep or awake, give thanks to God, who

*created and arranged all things for your benefit, to have you
know, love and praise their Creator.*

—SAINT BASIL THE GREAT[39]

*Every flower is fragrant through the power of the Holy Spirit,
in a delicate flow of aroma and tenderness of color; the beauty
of the Great contained in what is small. Praise and honor to
God, Who gives life, Who spreads forth the meadows like a
flowering carpet, Who crowns the fields with golden ears of
wheat and azure basilisks, and the soul—with the joy of contemplation. Let us rejoice and sing to Him: Alleluia.*

—AKATHIST "GLORY TO GOD FOR ALL THINGS"

For the Soul

As new parents we receive one of the most precious of all gifts:
the gift of human life. The love and joy a child can bring are
infinite. Moments spent holding our happy or sleeping baby may
be some of the most perfectly joyful and peaceful moments we
will ever experience. This gift comes with many challenges, such
as loss of time for other things, physical discomfort, emotional
strain, and mental exhaustion. We acknowledge these burdens,
and, in truth, they are also a gift—the gift of suffering that helps
us to grow stronger and roots out our spiritual passions.

We already mentioned how many seemingly mundane and
repetitive tasks are added to an otherwise full plate when a baby is
born: changing diapers, nursing or bottle-feeding, burping, bathing, rocking to sleep, not to mention washing clothes, dishes, you
name it. If we are not careful we can easily begin to feel resentful,

---

39 St. Basil the Great, *Homily V. In martyrem Julittam*, quoted in the *Prole-
gomena* in Nicene and Post-Nicene Fathers Series II, vol. 8.

if not of our new baby then of our partner, or simply of the easy life other people without tiny babies seem to be living. We can fall into despondency at the enormity and yet seeming insignificance of our new duties. We may begin to focus more on the difficulties than on the joys, dragging ourselves down in soul and body.

~

We must begin with thanksgiving for everything. The beginning of joy is to be content with your situation.

—SAINT AMBROSE[40]

~

At the start of this new era of our lives, whether we are first-time moms or have added a new child to our family, we have the choice to focus on our blessings and let joy into our hearts. How can we do this? How can we "make a joyful noise unto the Lord"? In our own lives, the answer is to start small. We start by turning our attention to the small aspects of our lives for which we are grateful and thanking God for them. Saint Basil's quote above is a simple yet powerful call to weave thanksgiving into the fabric of everyday life.

Finding the good in our lives and focusing on what we are happy to have can help to rewire and reorient our brain toward seeing the positive. Each of us will have trials and struggles, great and small, but if we allow these to become the focus of our attention, we will miss the chance to be grateful for God's love and the many blessings we already have. We are reminded of St. Paisios urging us to be the bee who always seeks out sweet nectar and to "always see the good side of things," rather than being the fly who, although in a garden full of beauty and fragrance, "will ignore

---

40 *Living without Hypocrisy*, p. 143.

them and will go sit on top of some dirt found on the ground . . . and feel comfortable with the bad smell."[41] By facing the Lord in gratitude and prayer, we can more easily see the amazing beauty already present in our lives.

For Mind & Body

GIVING THANKS

When we first start to bring our attention to thankfulness, it can be hard to let go of the focus on our stresses and hardships. It makes sense for our survival to concentrate on the dangers and to try to solve problems. In day-to-day life, many of us spend much of our time trying to fix things, get things done, help loved ones in need, and make money to pay bills. This often leaves us in a chronic state of stress. Having a baby can be a reprieve from this constant action, but it can also bring in new worries.

While simply holding a new baby in our arms can fill us with profound gratitude, there are endless gifts for which we can be grateful—our lungs that breathe, our hearts that beat, and shelter over our heads. Seeking this awareness and intentionally thanking the Lord for the wonders in our life will strengthen our ability to feel grateful.

SASHA

When my first was just born and my husband went back to work after a few weeks, I began to feel really overwhelmed. Coming from managing my own busy medical practice, I was now alone in the doldrums, or so it seemed, of this tiny human's constant needs. My son nursed all the time, then

---

41 Priestmonk Christodoulos, *Elder Paisios of the Holy Mountain* (Athos, Greece: Holy Mountain, 1998), pp. 43–44.

would immediately fall asleep only to be awake and hungry again a few moments later. I was jealous of my husband's seeming freedom and afraid of the profound solitude I felt at home.

We both recognized what was happening right away and came up with a plan to build in time for me to care for my still-aching body and physical needs. We also built in time for a practice we called "baby-gazing"—five to ten minutes that I would spend gazing at this precious gift in all of his glory: his tiny toes, the way his mouth moved and his eyes opened and closed, the gentle movement of his breathing, the noises he made. This was an invaluable exercise for me. We are so programmed, in our fallen state, to dwell on the negative (called *negativity bias* in psychology). Making time to notice what is good and right, and thank God for it, is a powerful antidote.

➤ PRACTICE ◄

Baby-Gazing

As Sasha shared above, simply sitting and gazing at your baby can be a gift to yourself as well as another way to cultivate gratitude amidst the often monotonous moments of newborn life. If you are a task-oriented person, it can be hard to let go and just *be*. So instead, "task" yourself with baby-gazing.

There is no need to prepare for this practice. Whenever you find yourself with a child in your arms, that is your moment. Just pause. Pause whatever daydream you were in the midst of and bring all your attention to your baby. Look at this amazing gift—this tiny human, fully formed in God's image. See your baby's little hands and fingernails, even notice how the creases of your baby's hand are formed. Watch your baby's breathing and his belly as the breath moves in and out. If you like, place your hand on your baby's chest and feel the miracle of her tiny heart—it beats so fast! Use your senses. How does your baby smell? What sounds is your baby making? What else can you notice? What a blessing this baby is—a gift from God that can give us such joy and also teach us so much that we need to learn.

Stay present with this experience for as long as you like and your baby allows. Practice as often as you can. We use this practice as a way to stay present in our life and to free ourselves from the distractions of our own mind. We also use the practice as prayer, praising "the beauty of the Great contained in what is small."[42]

---

42   From the Akathist hymn, *Glory to God for All Things*.

DAY 13

Theotokos

The Mother of God, Joy of All Who Sorrow

As soon as we cry out to her she rushes to our help. You don't even finish saying, "All-holy Theotokos, help me" and at once, like lightning, she shines through the nous and fills the heart with illumination. She draws the nous to prayer and the heart to Love.

—ELDER JOSEPH THE HESYCHAST[43]

When you are about to pray to our Lady the Holy Virgin, be firmly assured, before praying, that you will not depart from her without having received mercy. To think thus and to have confidence in her is meet and right. She is the All-Merciful Mother of the All-Merciful God, the Word, and her mercies, incalculably great and innumerable, have been declared from

---

43   "On the Mother of God: Quotes from Church Fathers," Antiochian
      Orthodox Christian Archdiocese, accessed August 28, 2020, http://ww1.
      antiochian.org/mother-god-quotes-church-fathers.

all ages by all Christian Churches; she is, indeed, an abyss of
mercies and bounties.

—SAINT JOHN OF KRONSTADT[44]

It is truly right to bless you, O Theotokos, ever blessed and
most pure, and the Mother of our God. More honorable than
the cherubim, and beyond compare more glorious than the
seraphim, without corruption you gave birth to God the
Word. True Theotokos, we magnify you.

—TRADITIONAL PRAYER TO THE THEOTOKOS

For the Soul

We end this section on maternal virtues by looking to our greatest example of a mother, the Theotokos. Mary stands as a shining example of love, virtue, and motherhood, present everywhere in our Faith. Her image surrounds us in our churches and homes; we celebrate her in many of the Great Feasts—her nativity, her entrance into the temple where she spent her youth, the Annunciation, and her repose, as well as the day she bore our Lord and God and Savior Jesus Christ and became a mother. Just as we refer to God as our Father, the Theotokos is, in many ways, a mother for us all.

If we do not already pray routinely to the Theotokos, we can see from the quotes above the benefits that such prayers provide. Already formal prayers to her permeate our morning and evening prayers, our liturgy, and the special services of Great and Holy Lent. In our Orthodox Faith, she is revered as holier than all the saints and angels, known to some as *Panagia*, a Greek word meaning "the Most Holy." And yet she was a woman of flesh

---

44   *My Life in Christ*, p. 43.

and blood, just as we are. Like us, she was a human woman who became a mother tasked with raising a child.

We may struggle to comprehend Mary and how she attained such purity that she was found "highly favored" (Luke 1:28). In thinking of Mary, it is important to remember that her entire life was lived for and with God. Her parents were pious and devout Jews, and even her conception (a date celebrated in the Ortho-dox Church) was the fruit of years of prayer and patience. From the age of three Mary lived in the temple where, it is said, she was allowed into the Holy of Holies—the most sacred part of the temple, where only the high priests gained entrance. We can only imagine the depth of love and beauty that grew in her soul from being so close to God.

Mary was a woman of profound humility, calmness of soul, and deep love—truly, qualities that all of us as mothers strive to embody. Developing this love and virtue as mothers can seem daunting. In her book *The Maternity of Mary*, Nancy Holloway gives us a glimpse of how we can begin to work toward Mary's example through the fullness of our faith.

To emulate Mary's love in today's secular, hectic, distracting, consumer-driven, fast-paced, and increasingly violent culture is the primary challenge for the Christian. This is the narrow way of which our Lord speaks. Only by being supported by the Church's prayers and worship, the rich legacy of the Church Fathers, and devotion to the Scriptures can we be faithful and discerning as we live out lives of love in such a treacherous world. And with Mary as the archetype of the golden threads of love and prayer—our model, guide, and intercessor—we

can persevere in the call to be changed from glory into glory
as we grow into the likeness of her Son.[45]

As the icon of the Mother of God Enthroned (*Platytéra*) depicts in our churches, the Theotokos is more spacious than the heavens. We reach out to her in prayer, in struggle, and in love, asking for her intercessions, because when she bore Christ, she contained the whole of creation and the universe in her womb, filling her with limitless love. She is a mother to all of us, and through her love and obedience to God she gave us her Son, who brought us life. While we are in the early stages of our journey of motherhood with this child, let us find ways to emulate Mary's virtuous and loving life and connect with her in our daily prayer.

SASHA

During Lent a few years ago I organized a psalter group inspired and led by the psalter companion book *Songs of Praise* by Sylvia Leontaritis of the *Orthodox Mom* blog (Ancient Faith Publishing, 2018). In one section she discussed the beautiful practice of writing a letter to the Theotokos. When I first read about this practice I was totally awed. I had never thought of praying to the Theotokos in this way. In fact, I will admit that I rarely prayed directly to the Theotokos at all.

Since reading this I have started keeping a small icon of the Theotokos by my bedside and picking it up as I get into bed. Gazing at the icon, I simply pour out all my concerns about how I am living my life as a mother, woman, and fallen human, and I ask for her guidance and intercession.

---

45   Nancy Holloway, *The Maternity of Mary* (Lexington, KY: Nancy Holloway, 2016), p. 87.

I have found the practice truly life-changing. There is so much I fear I do wrong, and there are so many worldly temptations I worry about keeping my children safe from— and yet I only have so much power to protect my children, and the rest is from God. *We are in God's hands!* What better way to seek divine intervention in all the issues of motherhood than to ask for the help of our own divine Mother ?

∼

Pray to the Theotokos. She is there with you and wants to help you.

—ANGELA, ORTHODOX MOTHER

∼

PRAYERS TO THE THEOTOKOS

Praying to the Theotokos is a great resource for everyone. For mothers, we especially like the *Akathist to the Mother of God: Nurturer of Children*. Below, we offer a prayer believed to be one of the earliest recorded in Christian history.[46] It is a simple and beautiful prayer asking for Mary's intercession.

✛ PRAYER ✛

Beneath your compassion we take refuge, Theotokos,
do not overlook our prayers in the midst of tribulation,
but deliver us from danger, O only pure, only blessed one.

---

46   Ibid., p. 46.

For Mind & Body

OUR MOTHERS

Our own mothers are important figures in shaping our perceptions, expectations, and identities as we become mothers. We may have been raised by our birth mother, an aunt, godmother, grandmother, adoptive mother, or someone else who took us into their home. We may not have had a mother to raise us if she died or left our family. Our experience of our mother or her absence will inform and guide our understanding, identity, and hopes for our own motherhood.

We may have had a loving and kind mother we hope to emulate, or maybe we suffered at our mother's hand and hope to be very different with our own children. We could even have had a wonderful mother and yet still hope to raise our children in a different way. As we take this step forward in our mothering journey, it can be helpful to acknowledge our feelings and the influence our mothers had on us. Even if we had an ideal loving and committed mother, we may have our own insecurities about being as successful as she was, or we may be holding onto small resentments or pain. Consciously praying for the soul of our mother, whether she is living or dead, and praying to be at peace with her can help in our own spiritual life and mothering.

➤ JOURNALING ◄

Reflecting on Our Mothers

Depending on our own experience, this exercise will be more or less difficult. If we had a particularly painful childhood with our mother, we can undertake this at a time when we feel ready to bring up these feelings and make sure we have support from our husband, friends, counselor, and priest to help us process them.

Start by just writing about your mother. Write what is in your heart. If you like, you can use these prompts to help you get started:

» What were the most important things you learned from your mother?

» What are your happiest memories of her?

» When did you feel most safe with her?

» What was painful about your relationship with her?

» What would you want to tell her if you could say anything to her?

» How do you hope to be like her as a mother?

» How do you hope to be different?

These writings and reflections are helpful in sorting out what we want to carry forward with us from our own experience of being mothered, and in defining our identity as a mother. Feelings that arise can be a good starting point for confession or for conversations with our own mother, if possible.

At the end of this exercise, and any time you feel moved to pray for your mother, we offer this prayer:

✟ PRAYER FOR OUR MOTHERS ✟

Dear Lord, thank You for blessing me to be a mother. I pray that I may be worthy of Your gift. Have mercy on me in my weakness. I pray for the soul of my mother. I pray that she is united with You in earthly life and after death. Guide her to You. Help me to emulate her virtues and learn from her struggles. Have mercy on her. I pray You to soften my heart and help me to forgive her any wrongs she has done me— real or perceived. I am grateful for the gift of life she gave me. Keep us both in your mercy forever. Amen.

PART IV

Passions of the Soul

We need challenges if we are to develop spiritually, and God can send those challenges through our spouses and our children. From the asceticism of those early days when a baby cries out in the middle of the night and pulls us from our warm bed, to the nights when high fevers or stubborn symptoms call us to prayer as we worry about the health of our children, we are denying ourselves and serving someone else, someone smaller and weaker, someone who relies on us. More than any simple fast, this kind of asceticism, offered up in love and with real personal sacrifice, will yield spiritual fruit.[1]

—ELISSA BJELETICH, *RAISING SAINTS* PODCAST

---

1   Elissa Bjeletich, "Parenting: Struggling Toward Salvation," March 3, 2017, in *Raising Saints* podcast, https://www.ancientfaith.com/podcasts/raising-saints/parenting_struggling_toward_salvation.

DAY 14

Remembrance of Wrongs

Letting Go of Resentment to Make Room for Love

He who has obtained love has banished revenge; but he who nurses enmities stores up for himself untimely labours.

—SAINT JOHN CLIMACUS[2]

If you harbour rancour against anybody, pray for him and you will prevent the passion from being aroused; for by means of prayer you will separate your resentment from the thought of the wrong he has done you. When you have become loving and compassionate towards him, you will wipe the passion completely from your soul. If somebody regards you with rancour, be pleasant to him, be humble and agreeable in his company, and you will deliver him from his passion.

—SAINT MAXIMOS THE CONFESSOR[3]

---

2   *Ladder*, p. 87.
3   St. Maximos the Confessor, "Four Hundred Texts on Love" 3.90, *The Philokalia*, vol. 2, p. 97.

You are angry with your neighbor, your brother, and say of him: "He is such and such—a miser, malicious, proud," or that he has done this and that, and so on. What is that to you? He sins against God and not against you. God is his judge, not you: unto God he shall answer for himself, not to you. Know yourself, how sinful you are yourself, what a beam you have in your own eye; how difficult it is for you to master and get the better of your own sins; how afflicted you yourself are by them; how they have ensnared you—how you wish for indulgence from others towards your own infirmities.

—SAINT JOHN OF KRONSTADT[4]

For the Soul

Bringing a new child into our lives can open a chasm of love we may be unaware existed within us. Even if we haven't yet fully encountered this wellspring just two weeks into life with our new child, we can hold faith that we will discover it. This love we have for our children is just a taste of the love that God has for us, His children. God loves us regardless of our past mistakes. He loves us in all our shapes, sizes, and colors, no matter our background, our DNA, or our abilities or disabilities. God's love for us is perfect. Our love for our children, ourselves, and each other is a work in progress, and remembrance of wrongs is its enemy. Saint John writes it is a "nail stuck in our souls."[5] When we hold onto the memory of wrongs others have done to us, we stifle our ability to love fully. Ultimately, then, letting go of these memories through forgiveness is an act of love for ourselves and others.

As Christians, we know that we must forgive. Every time we

---

4   *My Life in Christ*, p. 249.
5   *Ladder*, p. 87.

recite the Lord's Prayer we are reminded that forgiveness is necessary if we are to stand before God at the final judgment with hopes of being forgiven. By opening our hearts and forgiving, we allow for our own forgiveness. Jesus counsels us, "For if you forgive men their trespasses, your heavenly Father will also forgive you" (Matt. 6:14). Forgiveness allows for the cleansing and healing of our souls that we seek from God in confession and through repentance.

Like repentance, forgiveness isn't something we do once and are done. Sage guidance given in confession by Sarah's parish priest, Fr. David, is that "forgiveness is something we do again and again, even when we don't feel ready." Sometimes it seems the thing done to us was so grievous that we can't forgive—we are too hurt, too shamed, too angry to think of forgiving. In these moments we must pray to keep the roots of these passions from taking hold in our own hearts. This is when we must ask God to help us forgive and to soften our hearts so that we are able to forgive. In these cases, and especially when the actions done to us take long to heal and affect us deeply, forgiveness is a continual action. We make a daily choice to forgive, to pray to grow in forgiveness, and to ask God to heal us so our wounds do not fester.

⁓

When, after much struggling, you are still unable to extract this thorn, you should apologize to your enemy, even if only in word. Then perhaps you may be ashamed of your long-standing insincerity to him, and, as your conscience stings you like fire, you may feel perfect love towards him.

—SAINT JOHN CLIMACUS[6]

⁓

6   *Ladder*, p. 88.

When we become mothers, we are given the chance to deepen our spiritual commitment and clear out as best we can the pains and grudges of our pre-child lives. Letting go of the wrongs that have injured us and forgiving—even if only in word at first—is an important step in our spiritual growth.

As well as forgiving the wrongs done to us, we need to forgive ourselves. Forgiveness of self is a tremendous tool for a new mother. We will make many mistakes, some of which may even have significant consequences for our children; and yet we cannot fall into despair. We must have faith that even our own failings can be made whole through God's love.

In sharing the spiritual wisdom of ascesis, Orthodox theologian and writer Tito Colliander writes, "Do not root around in the soil of your old sins."[7] It is an uncomfortable image that evokes the reality of what we do when we dwell in our prior sinful behavior. When we have confessed and repented of our sins, we are not to look back as Lot's wife did. Instead, we are to look toward God and allow the places marred by sin to be purified in the cleansing fire of His love. This is the gift of God's forgiveness, and in this we forgive ourselves and move forward.

> ➤ **PRACTICE** ◄

Cultivating Forgiveness

As we try to uproot bad thoughts about others from our hearts, we focus on seeing others as children of God who are also struggling and falling down, also vulnerable to temptation and death. We can focus on forgiving others

---

7   Tito Colliander, *The Way of the Ascetics* (Crestwood, NY: St. Vladimir's Seminary Press, 1960), p.74.

to aid in our struggle, helping to uproot the seeds of anger before they blossom into contempt.

We needn't look hard to find moments for practice. Anytime we notice anger or resentment beginning to stir, we can seek out the cause—which is often a mix of frustration with ourselves and with others—and practice simply saying quietly to ourselves, *I forgive you.* We may be directing this forgiveness outward or inward—perhaps both. Even if the words feel insincere at first, we can keep saying them until we notice the tightness of the passion beginning to soften. Our partner is home later than promised? *I forgive you.* Our baby wakes up only moments after we tried for so long to soothe her to sleep? *I forgive you.* Someone cuts us off in traffic or honks at us as we sleepily make a slow turn? *I forgive you.* We spill some of the precious milk we just worked so hard to pump? *I forgive you.* It sounds so simple and almost silly, and yet it is a radically effective practice.

While we know as Orthodox Christians the power of forgiveness—while we ask it constantly of our Lord and Savior Jesus Christ in the Jesus Prayer—many of us do not practice it regularly and intentionally. These simple words have an incredible power to grow forgiveness in our hearts as a learned and practiced capacity.

For Mind & Body

GOOD POSTURE AND TENSION RELIEF

Holding on to emotional pain can also bring about physical pain and tension. To help ease our physical tension, we can adopt simple habits throughout the day to give us relief. Whether you bottle-feed or breastfeed, your back in these first weeks is likely sore. Because you are tired and focused on the tiny bundle in your arms, you tend to hunch forward, curling around your little one. If you are breastfeeding, this poor posture is often exacerbated as you try to bring your breast down to the baby in your lap. Keeping plenty of pillows handy will support you and your baby while feeding. In an ideal nursing posture, the spine is straight with the ears over the shoulders, not hunched forward. This will require setting yourself up well each time you nurse, at least in the early days.

In addition to being mindful of posture, take time for some gentle stretching. Try doing gentle neck and shoulder rolls while feeding baby. You will have plenty of moments for practice! A guided audio version of a stretching exercise for this day can be found on our podcast, *A Sacred Beginning,* on ancientfaith.com.

DAY 15

Slander

Loving Our Neighbors as Ourselves

When we see one of our athletes in Christ in bodily suffering and infirmity, let us not maliciously seek to learn the explanation of this illness, but rather with simple and genuine love, let us try to heal him as though he were part of our own body, and as a fellow warrior wounded in the fray.

—SAINT JOHN CLIMACUS[8]

You cannot be too gentle, too kind. Shun even to appear harsh in your treatment of each other. Joy, radiant joy, streams from the face of one who gives and kindles joy in the heart of one who receives. All condemnation is from the devil. Never condemn each other, not even those whom you catch committing an evil deed. We condemn others only because we shun knowing ourselves. When we gaze at our own failings, we see such a morass of filth that nothing in another can equal

---

8   *Ladder*, p. 169.

153

it. That is why we turn away, and make much of the faults of others. Keep away from the spilling of speech. Instead of condemning others, strive to reach inner peace. Keep silent, refrain from judgement. This will raise you above the deadly arrows of slander, insult, outrage, and will shield your glowing hearts against the evil that creeps around.

—SAINT SERAPHIM OF SAROV[9]

If you cannot close the mouth of a man who disparages his companion, at least refrain from joining him in this.

—SAINT ISAAC THE SYRIAN[10]

For the Soul

Slander, often thought of these days as simply gossip, is so commonplace and part of our culture that it can seem innocuous most of the time. This is a façade assumed by evil. As we read in the quotes above and will discuss in this chapter, guarding our tongues will benefit our souls and those around us. Historically, many cultures explicitly recognized the serious nature of gossip. In the Talmud, the written Jewish Law, gossip is compared to murder, for it too is irrevocable. A Russian proverb Sasha's great-grandmother would often quote is, "A word is not a sparrow. Once it flies out, you won't catch it."

Many if not all of us know the sting of being the topic of gossip, and many of us spend considerable time and effort trying to avoid falling prey to the criticism of others. What a waste of our precious time and gifts! We must repeatedly remind ourselves

9   St. Seraphim of Sarov, Yquotes.com, accessed March 15, 2021, http://yquotes.com/seraphim-of-sarov/130193/#ixzz6oY65kDgy.

10   Bro. Smith SGS, *A Monk's Topical Bible E–K* (Jasper, FL: Revelation-Insight Publishing, 2011), p. 255.

that we can only truly change ourselves. While gossip will always exist in our fallen world, we can choose not to partake in it.

⌁

A weak person prays that no one slanders him, a courageous person prays that God will help him not to slander others, neither in word nor thought.

—SAINT AMBROSE[11]

⌁

When we become mothers we develop a completely new skill set, and we often gain a new set of guiding principles for how we should act, how we should care for our babies, and how we (and others) should mother. We should breastfeed/give formula! We should hold the baby for naps/put him down in the crib! We should go back to work/stay home! The list is endless, even if we include only issues that come up in the first few months of life. The desire to do this right is so strong and the risks feel so high that when we see others doing things differently than we do, it is so tempting to judge and so disheartening when we feel judged.

These judgments often come from a place of ignorance. Others' relationships with God, the inner state of their soul and their struggles, are hidden from us. Saint John describes knowing one who "sinned openly and repented secretly."[12] We do not see the intimate details of others' lives. Instead we see only what they choose to share on social media. This can inspire jealousy, anger, and sadness. The internet is rife with attacks on whatever people post; many will leap at the chance to put someone in their place. All of us have private circumstances, and we do not always know

---

11   *Living without Hypocrisy*, p. 67.
12   *Ladder*, p. 90.

why some mothers act as they do or make the choices they do. We too have made choices and acted in ways that we later regret. We hope others will give us the same benefit of good grace.

⌒

If you judge people, you have no time to love them.

—MOTHER TERESA OF CALCUTTA[13]

⌒

Even in these modern situations, we can apply St. John's advice that one should not join in gossip or negative talk about others. Instead we should stop the conversation by saying, "I fall into graver sins every day, so how can I criticize?" Saint John reminds us that when we do this, something amazing will happen: "You will heal yourself and your neighbor with one plaster."[14] When we offer our own humility and acknowledgment of imperfection, we make room for others to be imperfect too. In this space we can have more supportive relationships with others, especially with other mothers as we all try our best to raise our children.

For Mind & Body

WHEN BREASTFEEDING DOESN'T WORK OUT

While we have focused on breastfeeding as a healthy way to feed babies, it is important to know that if you are not able to breast-feed, you have not failed your baby. Many women do not choose or are unable to breastfeed for a variety of reasons, and they can still provide everything their baby needs.

---

13 Mark Johnson, *Mother Teresa: Greatest Quotes and Life Lessons* (Sunnyvale, CA: Amazon.com Services LLC, 2015), p. 128.
14 *Ladder*, p. 90.

Starting in the early and mid twentieth century, advertising and fashion swayed popular opinion toward feeding babies formula. Most women were not taught or encouraged to breastfeed. The pendulum has swung the other way in our current time. While breastfeeding provides excellent nutrition, convenience, and negligible costs compared to formula, the "breast is best" pressure can be detrimental to the mental health of many moms.

Many women despair over their inability to breastfeed. If you have consulted your doctor and a lactation consultant, have prayed for guidance and support, and are still unable to breastfeed, give yourself the gift of acceptance. You are still the mother your child needs whether you can breastfeed or not. While you may mourn the loss of this aspect of childrearing, this is only one part of a lifetime of love and nourishment you can offer your child.

DAY 16

Silence

Quieting to Hear the Voice of God

The friend of silence draws near to God and, by secretly conversing with Him, is enlightened by God.

—SAINT JOHN CLIMACUS[15]

Where shall I place, child of Jesus, the spiritual intuitions springing from silence! How the eyes of understanding are opened and see Jesus in sweetness greater than that of honey! What new wonder is worked from legitimate silence and attentive understanding! You know these things, therefore compel yourself. A little has been revealed to you; struggle and you will find yet greater.

—ELDER EPHRAIM OF PHILOTHEOU, MOUNT ATHOS[16]

---

15 *Ladder*, p. 92.
16 Bro. Smith SGS, *A Monk's Topical Bible S–Z* (Jasper, FL: Revelation-Insight Publishing, 2014), p. 38.

My soul, wait silently for God alone,
For my expectation is from Him.
He only is my rock and my salvation;
He is my defense;
I shall not be moved.
In God is my salvation and my glory;
The rock of my strength,
And my refuge, is in God.

—PSALM 62:5–7

For the Soul

As a society we have a tendency to surround ourselves with noise. Whether with our own chatter, the radio, television, or notifications from our phone, we often avoid silence. Many of us equate silence with being alone; we fear the empty moments. Because of this we seek the exact opposite of what many of the great spiritual mothers and fathers sought—solitude. We turn a blind eye to what these warriors of the Faith knew: that silence and moments of stillness bring us into contact with the most important companion in our lives—God.

In these early days of motherhood, when we are more confined to home and constrained by our baby's sleep/wake rhythms, we can find the solitude overwhelming and feel quite disconnected from our community. Our newborn, while a true gift from God, is not company in the way we are accustomed to. Being alone with a newborn can feel quite lonely, especially if this is our first child or our other children aren't at home during the day. It can be tempting to fill the silence by spending lots of time on the phone, social media, watching TV, or listening to music, podcasts, or audiobooks. We certainly are not recommending enforced solitude, and we recognize the importance of community in a mother's life. However, we do recommend that here, as in other areas, we take time to be intentional about what fills our space.

⁓

The highest form of prayer is to stand silently in awe before God.

—SAINT ISAAC THE SYRIAN[17]

⁓

Silence holds tremendous power. In silence we are left alone with ourselves and God. In silence we are forced to listen to what is happening within us—our thoughts, feelings, bodily sensations, and the desires of our hearts. This can be challenging. Many of us are not accustomed to checking in with ourselves in this way. We may be surprised by the depth and breadth of emotions we come into contact with—sadness, anger, resentment, joy, worry, grief. We may begin to notice how tired, achy, and out of condition we are. We may also be startled by the thoughts that now enter our awareness—judgment of ourselves, anxiety, anger at our partner or family, even anger toward our baby (this can be very scary and is not so uncommon; if this is a struggle, see "Emotion Is Not Emergency" on page 190). All those sensations, thoughts, and emotions may exist inside us, even if we are not aware of them. It is important to recognize and potentially address them.

When we give ourselves space to be in silence, without constant distraction, we also begin to hear what is in our souls in a new way. In her book *The Next Right Thing*, Christian author Emily Freeman writes, "Silence and stillness are how I sift through the

---

17   As quoted in Orthodox Christianity, accessed March 15, 2020, https://orthodoxchristianity.info/the-highest-form-of-prayer-is-to-stand-silently-in-awe-before-god/.

day's input. The silence serves as a colander, helping me discern what I need to hold on to and allowing what I don't need to fall gently away, making space to access courage and creativity, quieting to hear the voice of God."[18] The more we are able to be with ourselves in silence, the better we become at understanding ourselves and our needs. We are better able to hear our own inner voice and God's call.

~

The voice of God is Silence.

—MOTHER GAVRILIA[19]

~

This connection with ourselves and our needs also helps us to be more in tune with what others need, including our babies. When we are able to rid ourselves of some of the audible clutter, we create space and quiet to connect with our baby even without words. While we do recommend talking with baby and singing to baby, we don't need to have the same flow of conversation that we might with another adult or even with older children. Nonverbal communication (through vocal sounds, facial expressions, and touch) is critical to babies' development and an important part of bonding. This provides an invaluable opportunity to practice letting go not only of external sources of noise but also of the noise we create.

It is important not only to create silence but to be intentional about how we break silence. What we say matters—a lot.

---

18 Emily P. Freeman, *The Next Right Thing* (Grand Rapids, MI: Revell, 2019), p. 27.

19 Nun Gavrilia, *Mother Gavrilia: The Ascetic of Love* (Pieria, Greece: Tertios Publishing, 1999).

Scripture is filled with warnings to avoid idle talk. In Matthew 12:36–37 we hear Jesus' warning, "But I say to you that for every idle word men may speak, they will give account of it in the day of judgment. For by your words you will be justified, and by your words you will be condemned." Proverbs 10:19 reminds us, "In the multitude of words sin is not lacking, / But he who restrains his lips *is* wise." In Colossians 4:6, St. Paul exhorts us that our speech be always "with grace."

We know we have fallen and will fall from this lofty goal again and again, and we thank God for His loving mercy. While this can feel like a high standard, imagine the peace that would surround us and our families if we all made more of an effort to invite silence in. *Our peace brings peace.* Not only is each word we say heard by God, but now our child(ren) are also listening. Can we use this time away from the world to begin to work toward speaking only words of grace? Can we speak less, listen more, and notice what is within us? Can we do all this to "draw near to God . . . secretly conversing with Him" and "stand silently in awe before God"?

SARAH

When my first daughter was a few months old, we visited my grandmother. My grandmother and I spent the morning enjoying the newness of my daughter and marveling at her little movements and facial expressions. As I was talking to my smiling baby while changing her diaper, my grandmother said to her, "Yes, you are happy, aren't you? Your mother talks to you like you are a person. Like you have thoughts and feelings." She looked at me and said, "That is very good, you know." In addition to being a wise and wonderful woman, my grandmother was a mother of three and a special education teacher. Her wisdom and approval meant a lot to me. I have not forgotten her words, and I believe the way we talk to our children matters.

For Mind & Body

WAYS TO CULTIVATE SILENCE IN OUR DAILY LIVES

We have many ways to fill our day and break the silence. Radios, TVs, phones, the hum of appliances, and smart speakers are so ubiquitous in many of our homes that we can't hear the sounds of the natural world. We invite you to take time as often as you can to turn all the electronics off, adding some silence to your day. If you live in a busy city, you might notice the sounds of traffic floating in. If you live in a natural setting, you may hear the call of birds or the chirp of crickets. For some of us, silence can be unnerving, so pay attention to how you feel; notice whether this is your reaction and why. Ask God to give you strength to meet Him in silence.

Other ways to create space for silence include:

» Find a time to be without your phone each day.

» While feeding your baby, just be with baby and don't multitask.

» Go for a walk without any distractions. Notice your own internal sensations and the world around you.

» Begin the practice of silently checking in with your own body by doing a body scan. Listen to our guided body scan on our podcast, *A Sacred Beginning,* on ancientfaith.com.

DAY 17

Falsehood

Living in Truth

Hypocrisy is the mother of lying, and often its occasion. For some define hypocrisy as none other than meditation on falsehood, and an inventor of falsehood which has a reprehensible oath intertwined with it. He who has obtained fear of the Lord has forsaken lying, having within himself an incorruptible judge—his own conscience.

—SAINT JOHN CLIMACUS[20]

Therefore, putting away lying, "Let each one of you speak truth with his neighbor," for we are members of one another.

—EPHESIANS 4:25

If we truly want to be saved, we have an obligation to take every care to love the truth with all our strength, and to guard

---

20   *Ladder,* p. 94.

*ourselves from every kind of falsehood, so that it does not sep-
arate us from truth and life.*

—ABBA DOROTHEOS[21]

For the Soul

Outright lying is something most of us try to avoid, but falsehood, or not being fully honest, can be a deceptively hidden passion. While we may try not to lie to others, being honest
with ourselves can be much harder. We may think of ourselves as
generous, and yet we don't give alms or help others when it isn't
convenient for us. We may believe that we are kind, and yet if we
honestly listened to the chatter in our head we would often find
ourselves criticizing others. Not being honest with ourselves about
who we are is a form of hypocrisy. We also display hypocrisy when
we say one thing and do another. As St. John explains, hypocrisy
is a form of lying. What we say in words we should do in action.
What we believe about ourselves should be based on the truth of
what is in our souls and the actions that result from it.

For mothers, especially first-time mothers, the knowledge that
a small being is now constantly looking at us for guidance and
understanding can be daunting. We are being observed and may
be forced to see ourselves anew through our baby's eyes. The eyes
that view us with endless curiosity and complete love learn from
us every moment. It is a great gift to be our children's teacher and
also a tremendous responsibility.

With this responsibility comes an opportunity to reflect on
ourselves. Are we honest with ourselves? Is what we claim is
important to us proven to be so by our actions? If we say that God

---

21   Greek Orthodox Archdiocese of Australia, *Voice of Orthodoxy* 19,
       no. 7 (July 1998), http://www.greekorthodox.org.au/wp-content/
       uploads/2016/09/VoO_Jul_1998_web.pdf.

is our Lord, are we ordering our lives in a way that puts God first? Saint Paisios captures the weight of this responsibility in saying, "Children imitate their parents even from the cradle. They pick up everything they see adults doing and record it on the empty 'cassette tape.' This is why parents should struggle to cut away their passions."[22]

Our children are sponges, soaking up knowledge, language, love, and teaching. They watch us to know how to be and live in the world. They can often surprise us by making us aware of things we don't see about ourselves. From this place of awareness, we have a new chance to be truly honest—in our words, in our deeds, and with ourselves.

As we change and grow into our new role as mothers, we can also become a better example of Christ for our children. We can practice truth everywhere. As St. John points out, fear of the Lord can keep us from lying and allow our conscience to guide us in truth. When we fear God, we have reverence and respect for Him, and this gives us strength to overcome our own sinfulness. In reference to fear of the Lord, theologian William Eisenhower writes, "As I walk with the Lord, I discover that God poses an ominous threat to my ego, but not to me. He rescues me from my delusions, so he may reveal the truth that sets me free."[23] If we follow God's path, we will be confronted with ourselves. If we humble ourselves before God and others, if we repent, if we examine our conscience in prayer, we will be faced with the truth.

Facing the truth will allow us to be honest with ourselves, our partners, and our children. We can ask for help when we need it

22 *Spiritual Counsels IV*, pp. 99–107.
23 William D. Eisenhower, "Fearing God," Christianity Today, February 7, 1986, https://www.christianitytoday.com/ct/1986/february-7/fearing-god-those-who-have-never-trembled-from-head-to-toe.html.

because we can admit that we have shortcomings. When asked how we are, we don't have to say "fine" when we are overwhelmed or lonely. We can let God help us through others by being honest. We can apologize when we've behaved badly, knowing we are fallible. In this way we will be modeling truth in action for our children. Despite the fact that we think we teach through lessons, we know we teach through action. American author Robert Fulghum's words ring true: "Don't worry that children never listen to you; worry that they are always watching you."[24]

SAINT EMMELIA (MAY 8/30, JANUARY 1)[25]

Cappadocia, Fourth Century

Saint Emmelia was an example of supreme faithfulness and commitment to God. She was the daughter of a martyr and married into a holy family. She is often called the mother of saints because five of her ten children were glorified by the Church. She is a model of maternal love. When her children were grown, she committed herself entirely to the Lord by founding a convent with her daughter St. Macrina, where she lived a harmonious life of virtue until her death. From the fruit of her virtuous life, we see that as mothers we have a great influence on our children's spiritual lives. Let us pray to St. Emmelia for the protection and guidance of our children's souls, and that we too may live our lives in the truth of our faith and bring our children with us.

---

24 "Robert Fulghum Quotes," Goodreads, accessed August 28, 2020, https://www.goodreads.com/author/quotes/19630.Robert_Fulghum.

25 David and Mary Ford, *Marriage as a Path to Holiness: Lives of Married Saints* (South Canaan: PA: St. Tikhon's Seminary Press, 1991), pp.181–184.

For Mind & Body

SCARY THOUGHTS

It can be helpful to know that most new mothers experience scary thoughts of one type or another. They are common, normal, and born out of the extreme desire to care for and protect our infants. Our minds sometimes overprepare for dangerous unknowns. We may think, "What if I drop the baby?" "What if the car seat isn't buckled?" and so forth.

Scary thoughts are worries, anxieties, impulses, fears, thought images, or obsessions that are intrusive and unwanted.[26] They can often feel overwhelming and cause a new mother distress as she wonders what is happening to her.

Prayer, self-care, and support from family and friends can help us to cope. In addition, we must work to recognize here, as in other situations, that our thoughts are merely thoughts and not the truth. Saint Paisios warned that when we begin to trust in our own thoughts we give them power to take hold of us: "Thoughts are like airplanes flying in the air. If you ignore them, there is no problem. If you pay attention to them, you create an airport inside your head and permit them to land!"[27] As we become more comfortable with our new role and with our baby, these thoughts will generally lessen. If, instead, they become intrusive and interfere with our sleep and ability to care for ourselves and our baby, then we should seek help. Many women are afraid to share these feelings for fear others may think they would harm their baby. Professional counseling and treatment can help tremendously when we are not thriving or feeling safe.

---

26 Karen Kleinman and Amy Wenzel, *Dropping the Baby and Other Scary Thoughts* (New York: Routledge, 2011), p. 22.
27 *Elder Paisios*, pp. 29–30, 48.

Searching for a counselor can be daunting, but there are many counselors trained in postpartum mood disorders. Postpartum Support International (see Resources) has a directory of therapists trained in helping women during pregnancy and postpartum. Although finding a Christian counselor may be your preference, a good counselor who may not be Christian herself will be able to support you in using your faith as part of treatment. When interviewing a counselor, simply ask, "I am a Christian and my faith is an important part of my life. Will you be supportive of this and able to integrate my beliefs with my treatment?"

Despondency

Paralysis of Soul

*Despondency is a paralysis of soul. . . . It accuses God of being
merciless and without love for men. . . . She [despondency]
reminds those standing at prayer of necessary duties. And,
brutish as she is, she leaves no stone unturned to find some
plausible pretext to drag us from prayer as with a kind of
halter.*

—SAINT JOHN OF CLIMACUS[28]

*So every time you fall, get up again and at once seek forgive-
ness. Don't hide sorrow in your heart, because sorrow and
despondency are the joy of the evil one. They fill one's soul
with bitterness and give birth to many evils. Whereas the
frame of mind of someone who repents says, "I have sinned!
Forgive me Father!" and he expels the sorrow. He says, "Am I*

---

28   *Ladder*, pp. 95–96.

not a weak human? So what do I expect?" Truly, my child this is how it is. So take courage.

—ELDER JOSEPH THE HESYCHAST[29]

We should not be despondent. In the sorrows we experience is concealed the mercy of God. How the Lord arranges our life is incomprehensible for us.

—SAINT NIKON OF OPTINA[30]

For the Soul

In *The Ladder of Divine Ascent,* despondency is described as the state of our souls in "spiritual gloom, indifference to the work of salvation and spiritual sloth."[31] Secular cultures may not define despondency in relation to spiritual life, seeing it rather as a loss of hope or courage. However, as Christians, we know that our hope and courage are from the Lord, and if these are lost, we too feel lost. From this place of confusion we can become apathetic to our spiritual life, losing connection with our true selves and the "peace of God, which surpasses all understanding" (Phil. 4:7).

The postpartum time can be disorienting, full of high highs and low lows. Being disconnected from work, church, and other communities, overtired, and perhaps underappreciated can leave us feeling downtrodden. Many of us wonder whether the way we are feeling is normal or if we might be depressed. We will surely have hard days, some worse than others. Struggle is a normal part of the transition after having a child, and asking for help during this time will be of great benefit.

Saint John describes how a lack of attention to prayer can drag

---

29   Elder Joseph the Hesychast, "Letter."
30   *Living without Hypocrisy*, p. 197.
31   *Ladder*, p. 95.

us into despondency. The early days of motherhood, with few extended moments for focused prayer and a hundred new tasks added to our list, can be a setup for despondency if we are not careful. We pray that this book and some of its suggestions may help to keep despondency from your heart right now. All five of our golden rules come into play here—using the struggle, recognizing how our peace shapes our homes, entrusting our lives and our children's lives to God, and starting where we are, as well as prayer, prayer, prayer in whatever way we can find it.

A simple and immediate start to keeping up our spiritual connection is to pray throughout the day. *Prayer is the way!* Seeking God in prayer is a tool to help us keep our thoughts on love and leave less space for temptations to creep into our heart and mind. Rather than overwhelming ourselves with the goal of keeping a full prayer rule during times of struggle, Orthodox writer Nicole Roccas suggests that "less is more." In her book *Time and Despondency*, she writes, "We need to hone the basics of facing and countering our destructive thoughts, of turning to God in the heat of our battles. We do this best by starting with short verses or phrases, learning to wield them and take aim with them as we would a sword."[32] The arrow prayers we shared in DAY 11: PATIENCE are examples you can use to counter despondency as well.

As we grow in strength and our rhythms and routines begin to take shape, we can add in Scripture reading, spiritual reading, repentance, and eventually confession to bring us healing. These are the actions of true spiritual self-care that will quell despondency and help sustain us through the glorious and difficult days and nights of raising children.

---

32   Nicole Roccas, *Time and Despondency* (Chesterton, IN: Ancient Faith Publishing, 2018), p. 114.

✚ PRAYER: PSALM 69 (KJV) ✚

This selection from Psalm 69 is helpful to say in times of need.

Save me, O God; for the waters are come in unto my soul.
I sink in deep mire, where there is no standing: I am come
into deep waters, where the floods overflow me.
I am weary of my crying: my throat is dried: mine eyes fail
while I wait for my God. . . .
But as for me, my prayer is unto thee, O Lord, in an acceptable time: O God, in the multitude of thy mercy hear me, in
the truth of thy salvation.

For Mind & Body

PERINATAL MOOD AND ANXIETY DISORDERS

While despondency is not necessarily a symptom of depression,
it is important to talk about how depression can manifest in new
mothers. "Perinatal mood and anxiety disorders" is an umbrella
term for a variety of disorders that can occur during pregnancy
or after birth. Postpartum mood disorders (PMDs), often recognized under the blanket term of postpartum depression (PPD),
can occur in mothers any time after birth through the first year
of the child's life or longer if untreated. Up to one in seven women
will experience postpartum depression, about half of whom will
never have experienced depression before.[33] It is important to note
that while it is not as common, fathers can also experience a PMD.

Many women are familiar with postpartum depression but
don't realize it can also include symptoms of anxiety. When

33 "Postpartum Depression," American Psychological Association website,
    accessed July 6, 2020, http://www.apa.org/pi/women/resources/reports/
    postpartum-depression.

anxiety symptoms are more prominent, a mother may have a postpartum anxiety disorder. She may feel worried or agitated; she may have racing thoughts, obsessive thoughts and behaviors, a feeling of dread, or trouble eating or sleeping. Given that it can feel so different from what we think of as depression, many who experience this will not recognize it as such. When suffering from a treatable postpartum mood or anxiety disorder, many women think, "I am not depressed, so I can't have postpartum depression. I know I don't feel good or like myself, but I guess this is just motherhood."

Feeling in a blur, unmotivated, overwhelmed, or irritable; being unable to get anything finished, crying, feeling numb, wishing to escape, feeling tired but not being able to sleep, or just not feeling like oneself are all common descriptions of how mothers experience a PMD. This can feel crushing for us as mothers—especially if we were excited about having a baby and expected motherhood to be fulfilling and joyful. We may think this is just what motherhood is like for *us* and feel guilty and ashamed because of it.

If any of the symptoms above describe how you feel, talk to your partner, your doctor, your priest, your mom, your sister, or your friend. Reach out for help by talking to someone who will listen. You don't need to suffer alone. In these moments we must remember the words of our Lord: "My grace is sufficient for you, for My strength is made perfect in weakness" (2 Cor. 12:9). We all struggle in different ways. For some of us, our struggle is a postpartum mood disorder, and this too is within the bounds of God's love. Getting help will help you and your baby to thrive.

~

I should have asked for help. I needed help. Desperately.
—ORTHODOX MOTHER

While many women feel guilty about feeling bad, we must remember that having a PMD is not a mother's fault, nor is it a spiritual failing. We become ill for a myriad of reasons, and although they can be difficult, our illnesses are part of our spiritual struggle. Many women, especially Christian women, do not want to see a therapist because they feel they should be able to recover on their own and with prayer. While this is certainly possible, and prayer is one of our most powerful ways to heal, medical treatment/counseling can be an important adjunct and can provide some needed objectivity and perspective. In the words of Saint Basil:

> So, then, we should neither repudiate this [medical] art altogether nor does it behoove us to repose all our confidence in it; but, just as in practicing the art of agriculture we pray God for the fruits, and as we entrust the helm to the pilot in the art of navigation, but implore God that we may end our voyage unharmed by the perils of the sea, so also, when reason allows, we call in the doctor, but we do not leave off hoping in God.[34]

Not all women with a PMD will need medication, but for some the proper medication can restore brain chemistry and make a huge difference. Medication can allow a mother to function, care for her baby, and begin to heal. It can be used just for a period of time; we needn't fear it will be addictive or require a lifelong commitment. Elder Epiphanios Theodoropoulos writes,

---

34 St. Basil the Great, "Question 55" in "The Long Rules," *St. Basil: Ascetical Works.*

The image which we can use to describe the relationship of soul and brain is the violin with the violinist. Just as even the best musician cannot make good music if the violin is broken or unstrung, in the same manner a man's behavior will not be whole (see 2 Tim 3:17) if his brain presents a certain disturbance, in which case the soul cannot be expressed correctly. It is precisely this disturbance of the brain that certain medicines help correct and so aid the soul in expressing itself correctly.[35]

Professional therapy can also be an important part of healing. It can help us recognize our thought patterns and allow our brains to function properly so that our souls may heal. A good therapist can help you make sense of what is happening, give you tools for moving forward, and be with you in the pain, disappointment, confusion, and difficulty you are experiencing. No part of our lives as Christians is without God; healing will also come to our souls as we reach out to the Lord for help and get spiritual support. We don't always see the full scope of God's plan, but we do know that our struggles are part of working toward salvation, and we are never outside of God's love.

SASHA

I have struggled with bouts of anxiety on and off my whole life. While, by the grace of God, this was not a severe symptom in my postpartum time, except perhaps as manifested

---

35 Fr. Stephen Freeman, "A Priest's Thoughts on Depression, Anxiety, the Soul, Your Body and Your Brain," *Glory to God for All Things* (blog), June 26, 2017, https://blogs.ancientfaith.com/glory2godforallthings/2017/06/26/priests-thoughts-depression-anxiety-soul-body-brain/.

in my being less patient and more irritable than usual, it has definitely been a battle for me at other times. Even early in several of my pregnancies, when I was homebound and disabled by nausea, I noticed despondency creeping in.

From my youngest years, at age six after my parents' divorce, until today, I have spoken with a handful of different therapists, each of whom opened to me a new aspect of myself. In my profession I also feel blessed to work closely with many wonderful therapists and psychiatrists. While each therapist is unique, I am universally impressed by their true desire to help people live well and find ways to overcome their struggles.

Recently, I recognized the need to speak with a therapist again. In the midst of the coronavirus pandemic, seeing patients and fearing that I might infect my own mother and family, feeling the physical toll of a much-desired fourth pregnancy, trying to begin a hybrid homeschool program with my children, and finishing the writing of this book, I wasn't sleeping well. I found my anxiety creeping in and beginning to affect my ability to be loving, caring, and present with my family.

Given that all things are done virtually in these pandemic days, I set out to find an Orthodox therapist with whom I could share not only my feelings but my faith in a meaningful way. I was blessed to find one locally. Since our first session together I have felt a profound gratitude for this chance to work on my own shortcomings while growing in faith. It was this therapist who reminded me of St. Paisios's words about not trusting our thoughts, which we shared in the last chapter. While we may not all have the opportunity to work with someone of our own faith, most therapists have the training to know that faith is a vital lifeline for many people and can help us better express our needs and find our own path toward peace.

DAY 19

Worry

Healing Our Unbelief

Therefore I say to you, do not worry about your life, what you will eat or what you will drink; nor about your body, what you will put on. Is not life more than food and the body more than clothing? Look at the birds of the air, for they neither sow nor reap nor gather into barns; yet your heavenly Father feeds them. Are you not of more value than they? . . . For your heavenly Father knows that you need all these things. But seek first the kingdom of God and His righteousness, and all these things shall be added to you. Therefore do not worry about tomorrow, for tomorrow will worry about its own things. Sufficient for the day is its own trouble.

—MATTHEW 6:25–26, 29–34

He who dwells in the secret place of the Most High
Shall abide under the shadow of the Almighty.
I will say of the Lord, "He is my refuge and my fortress;
My God, in Him I will trust."

Because you have made the Lord, who is my refuge,
Even the Most High, your dwelling place,
No evil shall befall you,
Nor shall any plague come near your dwelling;
For He shall give His angels charge over you,
To keep you in all your ways.

—PSALM 91:1–2, 9–11

Too great solicitude for worldly things is natural to an unbe-
lieving and faint-hearted man. And woe to us if we, in tak-
ing care for ourselves, do not confirm ourselves in our hope
in God, Who takes care for us! If we do not ascribe to Him
the visible goods which we use in this present age, how can
we expect from Him those goods which are promised in the
future?

—SAINT SERAPHIM OF SAROV[36]

For the Soul

It is common for us as new mothers to feel anxious and worried. Especially if we are first-time mothers, when everything
is so new and unknown, worry is natural. We may worry about
almost anything, from what type of diaper is best to whether our
child will get sick or have an accident. At these moments we need
to use our spiritual resources and remember our faith in God's
infinite love and mercy. Worries, fears, and anxieties can flood us
as mothers if we do not repeatedly guard our hearts and minds
against these attacks.

At the root of our modern anxiety is lack of faith. We say this

---

36   *Little Russian Philokalia, Vol. 1: St. Seraphim of Sarov* (Platina, CA: St.
     Herman of Alaska Brotherhood, 1978), p. 52.

with utmost humility and from personal experience. If we truly trusted and knew in our hearts that God is with us in all things, we would not worry about what might happen, for we would believe that all will be cared for by our heavenly Father. *We are in God's hands.* Especially in these moments of worry and doubt, we need to call out to God and ask Him for help: "Lord, help my unbelief!"

As St. Seraphim brings to mind in his quote above, reflecting on the blessings God has already brought us can help remind us of His love and care. We give thanks for the grace and gifts He has bestowed and cherish them as examples of His love to help protect us against our worry. Keeping these instances of His care in mind can build our trust in His continued mercy for us and help to ease our anxieties.

During our interviews with Orthodox mothers, we were struck by one particularly poignant example, shared by Sarah's priest's wife, of a way in which God cared for her in her forty days. We offer it here as a beautiful reminder of how God provides.

THANKSGIVING IN JULY

Often I am amazed at the tender care Our Lord gives to us Himself and through our Mother, His Church. He answers our prayers sometimes in ways we could not have imagined. Our needs are important to Him. It is so easy to forget this, to worry and to struggle on our own. Our Mother, the Church, helps us in many ways too, and for new mothers, the quiet time of the forty days after childbirth is a good example of loving care given to us.

I have always been very grateful for this quiet home time after my six pregnancies, given as a gift to me to rest, to recover, and to focus on each of my newborns. Knowing myself, I would not be able to take this time for myself, but through obedience to my Mother, the Church, and her Traditions, I was given the freedom to put myself and my family first, without thinking that I was burdening my husband with my everyday responsibilities outside the home. He willingly did so much, like shopping or taking children to and from school, without my having to ask. So freeing!

It was at one of these times of forty days that I truly saw God's tender care for me, and I will never forget this event, though it happened long ago. My son arrived in July, to the delight of his older sisters. It was such a blessing for us to once again have the gift of a little baby. When he was two weeks old, my husband had to attend a week-long conference halfway across the country. I knew I would miss him, but with my older children home, I had their company and could count on their help.

Not long after he left, I became ill with a stomach virus. I needed to be in bed upstairs with my baby near me so I could nurse him. I was worried that he or my other children would become ill too. How would I care for them when I was so ill myself? The weather did not help, as the temperature soared into the high 90s. We did not have any air conditioning. I worried I would become dehydrated and unable to nurse my baby.

Thankfully, by the next day, though I was still very weak, I was able to go downstairs. I knew I should try to eat something, and just then our doorbell rang. It was a neighbor that I did not know well. She handed me a large plastic container and told me that she was sorry because she had not brought me anything sooner. "I had this in my freezer," she told me as she turned to go. "It's from Thanksgiving."

It was homemade turkey soup. The perfect food. The perfect example of God's loving care for me. This was an important lesson for me not only not to worry, but it also taught me how I need to listen to my heart. I am the person with turkey soup in my freezer and could be given the thought of my neighbor, who may be in need. This good thought is probably the prompting of the Lord or my guardian angel. Will I listen? Even now, I think that I would be tempted to think that no one would want my turkey soup during a July heatwave. I need to be a better listener to my heart and not let worry dictate the way I could choose to do good.

That nourishing soup was delicious and helped me to recover quickly. None of my children became ill, and my husband returned to us safely. I am thankful as I remember the Lord's loving care for me, a sinner, and my neighbor's perfect gift.

—MATUSHKA FAITH

For Mind & Body

LOOK TOWARD THE LIGHT

Father Stephen Freeman, author of the Ancient Faith blog *Glory to God for All Things*, writes, "Despair comes when we look at the dark and forget the light."[37] An excellent way to remember the light is to recognize all that we have to be grateful for and thank the Lord for our blessings. In 1 Thessalonians 5:16–18 we are reminded that God's will for us in Jesus Christ is to "Rejoice always, pray without

---

37   Fr. Stephen Freeman, "It Is Good to Be Here," *Glory to God for All Things* (blog), May 18, 2020, https://blogs.ancientfaith.com/glory2godforallthings/2020/05/18/it-is-good-to-be-here/.

ceasing, in everything give thanks." Here we look at gratitude as a profoundly important spiritual practice that helps us remember and thank the Lord for the ways He is already caring for us, teaching us to trust Him, and ameliorating our worry.

Focusing on our many blessings changes our hearts and lifts us out of thoughts that tempt us to be dissatisfied with our lives. Saint Paisios called this dissatisfaction "grumbling." This grumbling "is caused by misery" and begets more grumbling. "You see, the more one grumbles, the more one falls into ruin. Sometimes the devil deceives us and makes us unable to be pleased with anything; however, one can celebrate all things in a spiritual manner, with doxology [giving praise], and secure God's constant blessing."[38] By keeping our hearts full of thanksgiving and fighting the temptation to complain, we invite God into our hearts.

There is no time like the present to start developing gratitude. Right now, as you read this, can you think of three things you are grateful for? They may be big things, such as your child or your health or the roof above your head; or they can be the simple, small moments that make your life unique, such as a chickadee landing on your windowsill or the smell of the fresh earth after rain. Take a moment today to combat worry by focusing on the blessings in your life and offering your joy over them to God. The journaling exercise below can help to get you started on a regular practice.

～

In short, let every action be a cause of your remembering and praising God, and lo! you will be praying without ceasing and therein your soul will always rejoice.

—SAINT PETER OF DAMASCUS[39]

---

38 *Spiritual Counsels IV*, p. 157.
39 Bernhard Christensen, *The Inward Pilgrimage: An Introduction to Christian*

> ➤ JOURNALING ◄

Cultivating Gratitude

This practice can be as simple or as intricate as you like. In general, we recommend trying to set aside a few moments to think of three things for which you are grateful. You may have more, but make sure you choose at least three. They can be small moments or deep joys. The power lies in the recognition of God's gifts. As we hone our ability to see the positive, we expand our lens and can begin to see the blessing and beauty of our lives in novel ways.

Another way to practice thanksgiving is to do it with a friend or spouse. When your children are a bit older, consider bringing this practice to them—even children as young as three can conceptualize this. A nice family ritual is to find time daily to allow each person to give thanks to God for some aspect of their day. Perhaps you can do this as a part of the daily meal, at evening prayers, or just before sleep.

SASHA

For years Sarah and I struggled to find ways to connect with one another when we weren't living in the same place. Sarah moved far away to Germany when she was first married. One way we found to connect briefly with one another more frequently was a daily gratitude text—just a quick text with three things for which we were thankful. This was before we had children, and it waxed and waned even then,

---

Spiritual Classics (Minneapolis, MN: Augsburg Fortress Press, 1996), p. 113.

but it was such a loving and connecting practice that I still cherish the memories of it today.

Anger

An Agitation of the Soul

If the Holy Spirit is peace of soul, as He is said to be and as He is in reality, and if anger is disturbance of heart, as it actually is and as it is said to be, then nothing so prevents His presence in us as anger.

—SAINT JOHN CLIMACUS[40]

During temptations of anger, pray for the one who has upset you: "Save, O Lord, and have mercy on ___, and through her holy prayers help me, accursed and sinful."

—SAINT AMBROSE OF OPTINA[41]

No matter how much the waves of temptation rise up against your soul, always hasten to Christ. The Savior will always come to your aid and will calm the waves. Believe that the Lord has providentially arranged such experience for your

---

40   *Ladder*, p. 82.
41   *Living without Hypocrisy*, p. 13.

soul's healing and do not reject them, seeking bodily peace and imaginary tranquility, for it is better to be shaken and yet to endure. If you will gain an insight from this, it will greatly lighten your struggle and you will gain more peace than if you do not.

—SAINT LEO OF OPTINA[42]

For the Soul

Anger is a challenging spiritual passion that lies at the root of much suffering. Our anger often arises from our own pride, fear, and feelings of being unworthy. Anger, psychologically speaking, is thought of as a secondary emotion because it is often used to cover up more vulnerable feelings. Underlying anger can be pain, fear, worry, resentment, sadness, and many other emotions. To avoid feeling these big emotions, we defend ourselves with anger and lash out at others.

We may lash out either externally or internally. Both are damaging to our souls. As in our war against any of the passions, the first step, according to St. John Climacus, is not to give voice to our sin. He writes, "The beginning of freedom from anger is silence of the lips when the heart is agitated; the middle is silence of the thoughts when there is a mere disturbance of soul; and the end is an imperturbable calm under the breath of unclean winds."[43]

We have already touched on many of the virtues that can help us to defeat anger—meekness, patience, thanksgiving, and repentance. Two of our quotations for today also point to obedience as a major weapon against anger. Saint John describes obedience of the lips as the first step and obedience of the thoughts

---

42   *Living without Hypocrisy*, p. 12.
43   *Ladder*, p. 81.

as the second step in combatting anger. The third step is to cultivate such peace of soul that anger has no foothold. Most of us will never attain this level of calm, and yet it gives us hope that each time we remain calm when we are tempted to anger, we strengthen our capacity to do so again.

During this time of change and upheaval, we may find ourselves with anger bubbling to the surface. In this postpartum period, hormones and sleeplessness as well as poor self-care and new worries can impede our ability to cope and can magnify our own response to feelings of anger. In this state our tempers are prone to flare much more easily than in the past. It can be hard even to try to keep the lips quiet in these moments—as if an internal filter has been removed. We may be surprised at the urgency and strength of our own reactions.

It may help to know that we are not alone and that these feelings are quite common in this stressful transition time. Times of transition are often where God places opportunities for growth. *Use the struggle to grow in faith and love.* Remember that, though our prayer these days may not look the way it did before, we may be finding more and more informal ways to include prayer. Any moment of struggle is a perfect moment for prayer. *Prayer is the way!* Let us remember Jesus' words: "Therefore I say to you, whatever things you ask when you pray, believe that you receive *them*, and you will have *them*" (Mark 11:24). One of the most influential theologians and speakers of the early Church, Evagrius the Solitary, stated it so simply: "Prayer is the flower of gentleness and of freedom from anger."[44]

---

44   Quoted in George Every, Richard Harries, Bishop Kallistos Ware, eds., *The Time of the Spirit: Readings Through the Christian Year* (Crestwood, NY: St. Vladimir's Seminary Press, 1984), p. 102.

➤ EMOTION IS NOT EMERGENCY ◄

Remember, most moments when we feel intense emotions are not emergencies. If your baby won't calm and you feel as if you are really losing it, put your baby in a safe place— either in a crib or bassinet, or buckled fully into his car seat. It is important to know that you can always put your baby down in a safe place for a few minutes when she is crying if you need to regroup. If you are losing your cool, it is more important for your baby that you recenter and calm down than that you hold and soothe him during every moment of crying.

For Mind & Body

MANAGING YOUR FEELINGS

All babies will cry at some point, no matter how well they are cared for and loved. Crying is an infant's method of communicating and releasing frustration. It can be disconcerting for us as parents to hear our babies cry. We are programmed to be bothered by crying so that we will attend to the needs of our babies. We may find that the sound of our baby crying brings up intense feelings. Some mothers find that their baby's cry activates stress, fear, or sadness. Some feel panic because they fear they may not be able to calm their baby, and they take this to mean they aren't good mothers.

Below, we offer a practice to use whenever strong emotion threatens to overtake you. Just as we would comfort a friend in a time of need, we can show ourselves kindness and compassion when we are having a hard time. Using the practice below can help you to sort out and move through what you are feeling, allowing you to pray about it and share your feelings with your partner. It can also aid in preparing for confession.

➤ PRACTICE ◄

Compassion for Yourself

This practice can be used any time you notice that you are struggling, but it is especially powerful when you are angry. You can also find a guided recording of this practice on our podcast, *A Sacred Beginning*, on ancientfaith.com.

If possible, put your baby down in a safe place and take a moment for yourself. Close your eyes and take a deep breath in and out, allowing yourself to settle. Check in with yourself. Can you identify why you are feeling angry or what is causing this moment of suffering? Do you notice stress in your body—tightness in the chest, cold feet, an upset stomach? What emotions are present in you right now—anger, fear, sadness, disappointment, loneliness, shame? What thoughts do you notice—self-criticism, memories of hurtful words, worries about the future?

Take a minute and acknowledge that you are suffering. It may not seem like a big deal, but this is hard for you right now. It can be helpful to simply say, *This is hard. I'm really struggling.* Then recognize and remind yourself that we all suffer sometimes. Suffering is a part of our fallen world; everyone has hard times, and everyone struggles. It may feel nice to put a hand on your chest or cup an elbow in either hand, holding yourself with gentleness as you would hold your baby. Just as being held soothes baby, your own gentle touch can soothe you as well.

Now is the time for prayer. *Prayer is the way.* In praying, find words that feel right to you. Some ideas are:

"Lord, may I be patient with myself and with others."

"Lord, I know that You love me. Help me to feel and receive Your love."

"Dear Father, I am weak; help me to be strong."

"O Heavenly King, Comforter, Spirit of Truth, come and abide in me and cleanse me of all impurity."

"O Lord Jesus Christ, Son of God, have mercy on me, a sinner."

"O Lord, enlighten my darkness."

Ask the Lord to share the burden of these stressful feelings and fill you with love. You may want to talk to your partner or write in your journal about this process.

This simple practice can be summed up in three steps:

1. Pause to recognize you are struggling (the hardest part!).

2. Acknowledge that struggling is part of all our lives and a key to our salvation. *Use the struggle to grow in faith and love.*

3. Call on our Lord's infinite love and mercy. *Prayer is the way.*

The more we remember to pause as we notice things starting to well up in us, the more we are able to deal with stressful situations before they get out of control or we lash out. In time, we will become more able to maintain peace in our souls and to share it with those around us. *Our peace brings peace.*

SARAH

Toward the end of my second pregnancy, I started having moments of intense irritability and anxiety. It got worse after my daughter was born. It was so strange and sudden. I would become overwhelmed with frustration, and it would strike with little cause. It panicked me because I didn't understand what was happening. Going to confession and praying when I felt under attack helped a lot, but I still kept feeling I was failing. I managed as best I could, wondering why I felt so angry when I was so happy to have my precious daughters.

Months after giving birth, I was taking a master class in postpartum mood disorders and started reading about postpartum anxiety and anger. Hearing the voices of other mothers sharing how they felt was like reading about myself. I couldn't believe it—I was a therapist and hadn't learned this was something women commonly experienced after childbirth! I'd just thought I was a weak person and felt very ashamed.

Once I could name what was happening, I felt enormous relief and was able to share my feelings. I got support from my family, started seeing a therapist, and relied heavily on prayer to find my way back to normal. I also learned that sleep deprivation was a critical factor for me. Once my daughter started sleeping well and I was getting more sleep, I no longer felt as if my nerve endings were exposed all the time. I started to feel more like myself and was able to cope with the daily ups and downs of motherhood.

PART V

Passions of the Body

*I cling to a deep and certain conviction that motherhood is—
in and of itself a spiritual practice—that the creator of wombs
and breasts placed deep spiritual fruit into the seasons and
tasks of motherhood.*

—CATHERINE MCNEIL[1]

---

1   Catherine McNiel, *Long Days of Small Things: Motherhood as a Spiritual
    Discipline* (Colorado Springs, CO: NavPress, 2017), p. 9.

DAY 21

Gluttony

Hungering for God

Blessed are those who hunger and thirst for righteousness,
For they shall be filled.

—MATTHEW 5:6

When heavy with over-eating, the body makes the intellect
spiritless and sluggish; likewise, when weakened by excessive
abstinence, the body makes the contemplative faculty of the
soul dejected and disinclined to concentrate. We should there-
fore regulate our food according to the condition of the body,
so that it is appropriately disciplined when in good health and
adequately nourished when weak. The body of one pursuing
the spiritual way must not be enfeebled; he must have enough
strength for his labors, so that the soul may be suitably puri-
fied through bodily exertion as well.

—SAINT DIADOCHOS OF PHOTIKI[2]

2   "On Spiritual Knowledge," in *The Philokalia*, vol. 1, p. 266 no. 45.

*In proportion as the man by God's grace lays aside the carnal
life, he begins to trample his carnal appetites under foot—he
alters his food, ceases to live for insatiable appetite: gradually
in his heart, faith, hope, and love begin to reign.*

—SAINT JOHN OF KRONSTADT[3]

For the Soul

The writings of the holy elders make it clear that gluttony is
related to our appetites, food, and the importance of fasting.
Saint John describes gluttony as a passion that leads us into other
sins. He sees connection to God as a means to overcome being
controlled by the passion of our stomach, while those who do
not know God "inevitably seek their pleasure in my [gluttony's]
sweetness."[4] By overcoming the call of the stomach, we are more
prepared to overcome the other passions.

To combat gluttony in our everyday lives, we have the ancient
spiritual practice, used by Jesus Himself, of fasting. In the
Orthodox understanding, fasting from food refers to abstain-
ing from animal products on Wednesdays and Fridays and
during the longer fasts throughout the church year. Sarah's parish priest, Fr. David, describes fasting as "giving up something
freely that we could otherwise have, to strengthen our will to
give up other things, like sin." An often overlooked part of fasting is to avoid overindulgence and complete satiety (or feeling
full), whether we are fasting from particular foods or not. In
our spiritual life, the way we feed ourselves can be used to help
subdue the will of our bodies, to allow the will of our soul and
spirit to grow toward God.

---

3   *My Life in Christ*, p. 135.
4   *Ladder*, p. 103.

Thankfully, the Church grants us economia in relation to fasting during pregnancy, the postpartum period, and the time we are nursing. In pregnancy, we often become much more aware of what we are eating and the nourishing power of our food choices. We may be more diligent in making sure we eat regularly and choose nutritious foods because we know we are feeding our baby too.

It may be easy for us, as new moms, to forget that we still need to take care of ourselves. In these early days with a newborn, we may find ourselves grabbing bites between feedings or even forgetting to eat. The emotional stress of new motherhood and its new demands on our time may tempt us to eat quick snacks and sweets in place of more balanced plates. In addition, sleep deprivation disrupts the hormones that regulate our appetite. Combine this with a healing and possibly breastfeeding body, and we have a mother who desperately needs nourishment to replenish herself.

The Church Fathers talk about the importance of nourishing the body for our spiritual lives as well. Saint Seraphim of Sarov is quoted as saying, "Every day one should partake of just enough food to permit the body, being fortified, to be a friend and helper to the soul in performing the virtues. Otherwise, with the body exhausted the soul may also weaken."[5] It is important that we fortify ourselves with nutrient-rich foods to keep our strength up and our spirit strong. We need to feed our bodies so that we will be physically and spiritually able to meet the demands of mothering a newborn. This lays the foundation for our own health and allows us to be caretakers for our children and families.

---

5   *Little Russian Philokalia, Vol. 1: St. Seraphim of Sarov*, p. 56. In her podcast *Food, Faith and Fasting*, Rita Madden uses St. Seraphim's views to introduce how following Orthodox counsel is good for our physical and spiritual health. Her podcast is a wealth of information, and she offers a lot of excellent suggestions and ideas.

When we do struggle with what, how much, how little, or when we are eating, we can give ourselves grace. *We start where we are.* Focus on eating something nourishing and enjoyable, while sitting down, at least once each day. This may be a lofty goal for some, but it is a good step toward self-care.

Ultimately it is not physical food and water that will sustain us, but spiritual nourishment. If we feel depleted, we need to refuel our bodies and also our souls. It is only in the living waters of Jesus' counsel that we will find true sustenance. In Isaiah 55:1–2 we hear God's call for us:

> *Ho! Everyone who thirsts,*
> *Come to the waters;*
> *And you who have no money,*
> *Come, buy and eat.*
> *Yes, come, buy wine and milk*
> *Without money and without price.*
> *Why do you spend money for what is not bread,*
> *And your wages for what does not satisfy?*
> *Listen carefully to Me, and eat what is good,*
> *And let your soul delight itself in abundance.*

For Mind & Body

FEEDING OURSELVES

Both of us follow some basic principles gleaned from our work and personal lives to guide us in our food choices. We hope you are being fed by others as much as possible, and we recognize that will mean eating what you are offered with a thankful heart. These guidelines are intended for when you are feeding yourself and your growing family.

Whole and Unprocessed Foods

We recommend eating as many whole and unprocessed foods as possible. *Whole foods* refers to meat, dairy, vegetables, fish, grains, legumes, nuts, and fruits. Try to get into the habit of checking food labels. The fewer processed ingredients, the better. The ingredients list should contain foods that are recognizable rather than a lot of synthetic ingredients and additives.

Healthy Fats

When our body is healing, and especially if we are breastfeeding and making milk, we need good fat sources. Avocados, olive and coconut oils, nuts, pasture-raised or hormone-free meats, wild fish, eggs, and dairy are all important sources of fat.

Fermented Foods and Probiotics

Our intestines are full of beneficial organisms, known collectively as our microbiome, which play an extremely important role in everything from digestion and immune function to mood and metabolism.[6] We can grow a healthy microbiome by eating traditionally fermented foods and foods rich in probiotics. Sauerkraut and pickles made without vinegar, kimchi, yogurt, kefir, kombucha, and probiotic supplements can all help to increase the microbial diversity in our gut.

Our baby's microbiome is also developing and will become an important part of his or her lifelong health. Human breast milk contains oligosaccharides, a prebiotic that feeds microbes in a baby's intestinal tract.[7] Your baby cannot digest this substance;

---

6   Ting-Ting Huang, et al., "Current Understanding of Gut Microbiota in Mood Disorders: An Update of Human Studies," *Frontiers in Genetics* 1098 (February 19, 2019).

7   L. Bode, "Human milk oligosaccharides: Every baby needs a sugar mama," *Glycobiology* 2012, 22(9): 1147–1162.

it is simply there to feed the microbes so that a strong colony can develop and strengthen your baby's immune system. If you are not breastfeeding, or if you or your baby had to take antibiotics before, during, or after the birth process, consider using an infant probiotic to help replenish the organisms your baby needs for a healthy digestive and immune system. Even mixing a small amount of store-bought kefir (1–3 ml once a day) into baby's formula can be beneficial. Note: avoid giving baby anything sweetened with honey during the first year of life. Honey can contain *Clostridium botulinum,* a bacteria which is especially harmful for children under age one.

Sugars

The processed foods so prominent in the average American diet have a lot of unnecessary added sugars to mask the absence of nutrients and fats and make foods palatable. As much as possible, try to eat only those sweets made with cane sugar, maple syrup, or honey. Try to avoid chemical and artificial sweeteners (such as sucralose and aspartame) as well as high-fructose corn syrup. Feeding your body whole foods, including whole sugars, will give you the energy and nutrients you need to heal. We don't mean to suggest you can't enjoy sweet foods—but consider fruits and natural sugars first, and then less-processed foods like homemade cake or real ice cream (the kind that contains only cream, eggs, and sugar) to give you calories that will energize and heal you as well.

Calcium

If you are breastfeeding, remember also to increase your intake of calcium through eating not only dairy products but also seeds, beans, lentils, almonds, tofu, and greens such as collards, spinach, and kale. If we don't get enough calcium, our body will start to take the extra it needs from our own bones, so keeping your intake up is important.

⌣

I was craving the wheatberry pudding [koliva] that is served at funerals! I could not get enough of it! I would add raisins to it and eat bowls and bowls of it along with fresh vegetables. I was also craving salmon. I would get canned salmon and dump it into a bowl and eat the skin! I know it sounds gross, but the skin and fatty acids of canned salmon are high in vitamins. I didn't tell anybody about the amount of salmon that I was going through; I knew that my body must be craving it.

—ORTHODOX MOTHER

⌣

A word of encouragement: While you may feel eager to begin getting back to your pre-baby shape and size, we urge you to focus on what your body needs right now. You are undergoing a tremendous transition in these first forty days. While we often put our own needs on the back burner as mothers, we should consider that for us to eat and drink well is as important to our child's well-being as our sleep. If, in general, we try to follow these guidelines and pay attention to when we are stress-eating, with time our bodies will find a healthy new normal. It took our bodies forty or so weeks to get to this state, and we do well to patiently anticipate it will take us forty or more weeks to gently make our way back.

SARAH

Writing this chapter was challenging for me. I am cautious about telling new mothers to watch how much they are eating or to be concerned about gluttony. I was hesitant to write about food and wanted to focus on other forms of gluttony—consumerism, social media, and self-indulgence. Sasha challenged me to look closely at what the Fathers have written about gluttony and why their thoughts could be pertinent here. I realized part of the cause of my resistance was my own struggle with food, including overfeeding myself at times of stress and especially when sleep-deprived. I used to joke that the amount of chocolate I ate was directly related to the amount of newborn crying that happened each day.

This is a place of growth for me, growing in obedience and self-discipline, much the same as with emotional stress. Learning to turn toward the Lord when I am feeling my temper rise to keep from yelling at my loved ones, and learning to take care of myself and my needs before I am burnt out so that I can be a strong and present mother to my children, develops the same discipline as learning to eat in a way that honors the body God has given me.

DAY 22

Chastity

A New Intimacy

Purity means that we put on the angelic nature. Purity is the longed-for house of Christ and the earthly heaven of the heart.

—SAINT JOHN CLIMACUS[8]

Children, I beseech you to correct your hearts and thoughts, so that you may be pleasing to God. Consider that although we may reckon ourselves to be righteous and frequently succeed in deceiving men, we can conceal nothing from God. Let us therefore strive to preserve the holiness of our souls and to guard the purity of our bodies with all fervor.

—SAINT NICHOLAS OF MYRA[9]

---

8   *Ladder*, p. 104.
9   St. Demetrius of Rostov, *The Great Collection of the Lives of the Saints* (St. Louis: Chrysostom Press, 2000).

Do not deprive one another except with consent for a time, that you may give yourselves to fasting and prayer; and come together again so that Satan does not tempt you because of your lack of self-control.

—1 CORINTHIANS 7:5

For the Soul

Saint John wrote about purity of heart and chastity for the monastic, helping to support the goal of celibacy. While celibacy is a noble vow, the path of marriage and family is an honorable course as well. In our Orthodox Faith we view sex within marriage as a joyful part of a couple's union. Sex between a married couple is blessed by God, and the couple becomes "one flesh" (Matt. 19:5). This is for the sanctity of the marriage, the benefit of both spouses, and in hopes of being blessed with children.

While sex is a means of connection for many couples, we also have chaste periods throughout marriage. There are times when we may not be physically intimate with our spouse, such as during postpartum, illness, and when observing the marital fasts of the eve of liturgy and fasting periods. In the quote from 1 Corinthians above, St. Paul instructs that these periods of abstinence, with the consent of both spouses, can be spiritually beneficial.

After birth a mother's body is healing, and postpartum sexual intimacy may well be far from our thoughts. After months of stretching and reorganizing, our muscles, bones, and ligaments need time to return to their proper positions. Our womb was opened, and from a medical persepctive, intercourse is not recommended for at least six weeks as it heightens the possibility of infection. While our partners likely witnessed the incredible work our body went through to grow and birth this baby, their bodies are not in need of healing, and they may have their own feelings about this extended period without physical intimacy. Making sure to keep communication open around this topic is important.

While sex takes a natural hiatus, the chastity of this postpartum time allows for the growth of our spiritual life as a family. In his book *One Flesh*, Fr. Lawrence Farley writes,

> *Sexual congress with one's spouse is good, for it brings one closer to the spouse, binding one more deeply in a one-flesh union, helping one to transcend oneself and value the happiness of another more than one's own. Its value is in its unitive power. But though sexual union with one's spouse is good, abstaining from such union is better, for it allows both the spouses to draw closer to God. Resisting something as basic to our natures as sexuality creates an internal pressure, an empty space, which can be filled by God's Spirit.[10]*

If we approach this time with love, prayer, and open communication, we can focus on growing together spiritually and as parents. With mutual love and the grace of God, spouses grow closer. Sexual intimacy will come again after our bodies have healed. In the meantime, we can pray together, hold hands, hug, look into one another's eyes, and marvel at the being we have brought into the world.

---

10   Lawrence Farley, *One Flesh: Salvation through Marriage in the Orthodox Church* (Chesterton, IN: Ancient Faith Publishing, 2013), p. 57.

For Mind & Body

BUMPS IN THE MARRIAGE ROAD

Having a child is a great blessing for a couple, but it can also bring new stressors. Communicating and relating after having a baby can be difficult. You or your partner may harbor resentment over changing roles and duties. Many new mothers feel very alone, even if they have a partner. Oftentimes a woman can feel alienated from her partner when the bulk of the care and demands of a new infant seem to rest on her shoulders.

The bodily weariness of pregnancy and labor really begin to take their toll when the infant arrives. New mothers often aren't sleeping, their bodies are sore, and most just want some relief. Because of the demands of the baby and the needs of the mother, the husband's physical and emotional needs often take a back seat. Fathers can feel left out and unimportant in these early days—a feeling that may be aggravated by lack of physical intimacy. These factors create a situation that can be ripe for discord between partners.

Parents of young children often experience a marked deterioration in marital satisfaction after the birth of a child.[11] It is important to remember that this isn't the way it will always be. We can be resentful, tired, and stressed, and still make it to the other side as a couple. In this new space we have a chance to grow and find an even greater depth of intimacy and care. When we struggle, when we are vulnerable with each other, greater intimacy can grow in our partnership.

It may be helpful to remember right now that in our marriage

---

11   B. D. Doss, G. K. Rhoades, S. M. Stanley, and H. J. Markham, "The effect of the transition to parenthood on relationship quality: An 8-year prospective study," *Journal of Personality and Social Psychology*, 96(3), 601–619.

ceremony we wore crowns. We were crowned in glory as rulers of our home. We were also crowned as martyrs because of the sacrifices both spouses make for one another. For many couples, this postpartum time can be the first time in a marriage when we see each other in true vulnerability, in sickness, with our defenses down, or in some cases with our defenses up. At these times especially, we are called to dig in and do the work of marriage—to love, sacrifice, cherish, and forgive. We strengthen our marriages by strengthening our faith and reliance on God. Our partners can never fulfill all our needs, nor can our children. Only God can wholly heal our broken parts with His love. This in turn helps us love our partner wholly and know grace and forgiveness in our relationship.

We can start by praying for each other. We can take care of each other, allowing our partner to care for us and accepting the shifting roles and duties of this time. Let your partner know how much he is doing toward the care of the baby by supporting and taking care of you. Making time for one another, time to talk and time to forgive, is very important in the start of our journey together as the parents of this new little soul.

➤ PRACTICE ◄

Caring for Each Other

Below are some ideas to help you bond during this time:

» Make time to be together and talk about it all.

» Pray together, and on your own, pray for your partner.

» Make time for physical contact—holding hands, cuddling together, with baby and without.

» Gaze into one another's eyes.

» Make a practice of routinely asking forgiveness of one another.

» End the day by reviewing together what went well and what didn't, and come up with a collective plan for the next day.

SASHA

When I was five, my parents divorced and my father moved back to England, his home country. They barely spoke for almost ten years. For me as an only child it was incredibly isolating and painful. I remember wondering why people waited until *after* they had children to get divorced. Couldn't they make up their minds earlier and spare their children the suffering?

Becoming a parent made me realize that having children may itself be what creates the rift in a marriage or exposes the differences that were already there. Having children definitely put a lot of pressure on my marriage—having to make decisions together about important things that will affect our children for the rest of their lives, having to really compromise and listen. There is so much new territory for each person to navigate, and we must do this together as a team.

While I worried about how having a second child would affect us after coming through the difficulties of the first, I see clearly now that having children has made us stronger as a couple and continues to do so. We are more in love than when we married. We each see the way the other loves our children, the sacrifices we each make for our children and for our family. We witness each other's growth into more giving, more loving, and more grounded individuals. Our relationship isn't always perfect, and challenges still come up, but we are able, with the grace and love of God, to use our struggles to grow together in faith and love.

Postpartum Hormones and Resuming Sex

Our postpartum bodies and hormonal mix are different than before or during pregnancy. The high estrogen levels of pregnancy have waned, oxytocin levels are higher from birth and breastfeeding, and our progesterone levels have dropped significantly since giving birth. All of this may leave us feeling emotional, moody, and not interested in sex.

Every woman's fertility and level of desire is different after each birth. Some women may start menstruating again a few weeks after giving birth, while others may not have their next period for over a year. Breastfeeding often delays the return of a woman's cycle, but this is not guaranteed, nor is it a reliable form of family planning. You can be fertile before your period returns; many women get pregnant during the first months after having a baby and never have a period between pregnancies.

Some women are ready to resume sexual intimacy after the initial six-week healing period (or even before), while others are not physically or emotionally ready for intercourse for many months. Resuming sexual intimacy after giving birth can cause some women a lot of anxiety, especially if they had a difficult birth experience. Our bodies most likely will feel different in the beginning. If we are breastfeeding, our breasts may feel uncomfortable, or we may feel that that their function right now is feeding our baby, not being a part of intimacy with our partners. Whatever you are feeling, it is important to share those feelings honestly with your partner so that he does not feel rejected or as if he is responsible for your lack of desire.

When you are ready to resume intercourse, remember that during breastfeeding, decreased estrogen levels cause increased vaginal dryness. To prevent a painful experience, prepare by having lubrication close at hand. When you are ready, make sure to share any fears or concerns you have with your spouse and perhaps your medical provider, and go slowly.

DAY 23

Avarice

Sharing Our Wealth and Joy

Avarice, or love of money, is the worship of idols.

—SAINT JOHN OF CLIMACUS[12]

Looking upon God's world, I see everywhere God's extraordinary bountifulness in the gifts of nature: the surface of the earth is like the richest table, prepared with abundance and variety by the most loving and generous of hosts. Every Christian, especially the priest, ought to imitate God's bountifulness. Let your table be open to everybody, like the table of the Lord. The avaricious is God's enemy.

—SAINT JOHN OF KRONSTADT[13]

Do you wish to honor the Body of the Savior? Do not despise it when it is naked. Do not honor it in church with silk vestments while outside it is naked and numb with cold. He who

---

12 *Ladder*, p. 121.
13 *My Life in Christ*, p. 46.

said, "This is my body," and made it so by his word, is the same who said, "You saw me hungry and you gave me no food. As you did it not to the least of these, you did it not to me." Honor him then by sharing your property with the poor. For what God needs is not golden chalices but golden souls.

—SAINT JOHN CHRYSOSTOM[14]

For the Soul

Today we reflect on the sin of avarice, or the love of money, which is often thought of as synonymous with covetousness or greed. Avarice is categorized under the physical passions as one that stems from a desire for material comfort. It has a deep connecction with our spiritual struggles and everything we have been covering to date—from renunciation and detachment through despondency, worry, and anger.

Saint John discusses almsgiving extensively in this chapter and condemns the act of amassing wealth as a pretext for charitable giving. In essence, he warns us about using our "honorable" plans for the future as an excuse for greed in the present. Almsgiving is a noble deed and indeed a necessary act for our spiritual well-being. But its primary spiritual purpose is not to provide for others (since we know that it is ultimately God who provides) but to help us let go of attachment to money, show love for our neighbor, and put our trust in God.

We remember the story of the rich man who asks Jesus how to obtain eternal life. Jesus replies, "If you want to be perfect, go, sell what you have and give to the poor, and you will have treasure in heaven; and come, follow Me" (Matt. 19:21). This advice is simple and yet profound. With these words, Jesus reveals that true

14   St. John Chrysostom, *Homilies on the Gospel of St. Matthew*, Homily 50.

perfection comes through detachment and non-possessiveness. He reminds us that treasure lies in being rich toward God and not in material possessions. It is not only in the act of giving but in the act of following Christ that we are saved. This advice is devastating for the rich man, who walks away sorrowfully.

While becoming mothers can prompt us to rethink our priorities, often helping us to appreciate human life more than wealth, it can also make us rethink our budgets and finances. Many of us begin to save for our children's future the very year they are born, putting monthly payments into the bank. We may also begin to make payments toward life insurance or into a fund to care for our children in case of an emergency. We may worry if we are not able to prepare in this way. We may find ourselves more reluctant to show financial generosity. This is normal and yet potentially dangerous. In his reflection on St. John's original work, Fr. Papavassiliou mentions this challenge for parents directly and quotes from St. Basil:

> *"But wealth is necessary for rearing children," someone will say. This is a specious excuse for greed; although you speak as though children were your concern, you betray the inclinations of your own heart. Do not impute guilt to the guiltless! They have their own Master who cares for their needs. They received their being from God, and God will provide what they need to live.*[15]

Before motherhood we may have been on the road to trusting our well-being into the hands of God. But it can be harder to avoid the trap of feeling we are solely responsible now that we have someone so tiny and helpless in our care. We must pray for God's

---

15   *Thirty Steps to Heaven*, p. 135.

help and continue to strive to lay our cares on the Lord. It will not be in the amassing of material wealth that we can best care for our children but in making our home a Christian home and raising them in the love of God. *We are in God's hands.*

As we become mothers, we begin to notice that much of our nurturing and giving turns toward our children. This is true not only financially but also emotionally. Right now in the postpartum period, perhaps more than any other time, we are singularly focused on ourselves and our family. It is only natural to turn the empathy and love we have been giving to our neighbors inward onto our own little brood. To some extent it is expected during this time that we will forsake those outside our immediate sphere.

As our period of rest and recovery comes to a close, we should be careful not to let this state become our new normal. These forty days are given us as a time of rest and recovery, away from work, church, and certain responsibilities, but the time to return and reconnect comes quickly. The way we redefine ourselves as mothers begins now and affects what comes later. Even at this time, when we feel that we give and give to our own family, do we have some small offering for others? A simple text or a short email or note can bring joy to another's day. Sharing our wealth at this time could take the form of sharing baby pictures with grandparents or family far away. Perhaps we could invite a friend over for coffee or visit a lonely neighbor with our new little bundle. The act itself need not be large—the effort is what counts.

Remember the widow and her donation of the two mites (Luke 21:1–4). Even now, as we may feel depleted and as if we have nothing more of ourselves to give, we are asked not to completely abandon care for those outside our own kin. As Jesus Himself explains in Matthew 12:46–50, our family is not only of our own flesh and blood. We may even find renewed energy and joy in the process of sharing the blessings of love and joy that have been bestowed on us. Love is something we never run out of; it is truly the gift that keeps giving. We find that in loving our children, our capacity to love is increased; therefore, we have more treasure to share.

> ▷ PRACTICE ◁

Filled with Grace

Even as we grow in love, there may be times when we feel depleted and poor in patience, love, and generosity. We may feel we can't attempt even small offerings of our wealth to others. Many times, we just can't do it. *We can't get up one more time. Our arms are done holding a crying baby, and we just want to be alone. We don't have any more love to give.*

In these moments, we can forgive ourselves and let the Lord share our burden. This is an antidote to depletion (along with a good night's sleep!). We all need to recharge. Especially in these moments, we ask for God's love to come through us to our child. We can let ourselves be His instrument. This doesn't have to take anything additional from us. His love can fill us and flow to our children as well as to those around us.

Lie down if your baby is sleeping (take a break!). If not, lay your baby next to you, or on your chest, or even safely in another room if needed. Close your eyes. If your baby is crying, cry with her if you need to. When you are ready, take a few deep breaths and imagine the love of God all around you. Imagine you are being held in the holy glow and love of our Lord. Let this love seep into your skin, warm you, relax you, flow into the center of your being, into your soul, filling all the dark, weary, sad spaces. Let His love renew you. Picture the warm glow of the Holy Spirit cleansing all your pain, frustration, jealousy, resentment, whatever you may be feeling. Let this love overflow out of you. Imagine it flowing to your baby, to your partner, filling your house with love, peace, and the calm of the Holy Spirit. Whenever you feel you don't have any more to give, call upon the love of the Lord to fill you and your home again.

For Mind & Body

GETTING HELP WHEN WE DON'T KNOW HOW TO ASK

Just as others need care from you, there will be times when you need practical help. Sometimes your partner may want to help in those moments when he sees you are burdened. Once it's visible how much you are struggling, you may not know what to ask for or how. We offer the following thoughts. If they resonate with you, consider sharing the list and letter below with your partner.

Rest. Sleep deprivation with a baby is real and can cause pervasive difficulty. Ask for support in getting rest. Plan your nap times. If possible get help with nighttime feedings. Have your partner take the baby for a few hours while you shower and rest.

Simple gifts of time. One of the biggest changes we hear about from moms, and have experienced ourselves, is a sense that we just don't have time for ourselves. We love our new child with all our heart, but we need some time to ourselves to grow into these changes. It's important that your partner acknowledge this and support you by giving you time to take care of yourself. Taking the baby for a walk, bottle feeding, bathing the baby, baby gazing, and time holding and bonding with the baby are important activities for dads too!

Help in the house. Different couples divide household duties differently. During this time of recovery from childbirth and/or care of a newborn, tasks may need to shift a bit. Ask your partner to help with some extra household chores (dishes, laundry, meal prep) so you can stay off your feet a bit more and rest.

Love and support. Your partner can let you know that he loves you and will be there for you, even if you are struggling and aren't feeling or acting your best.

Support in getting help. If you are struggling emotionally and need professional help, your partner may be the first to notice. You can check in with him and also ask him to come with you to the doctor or therapist to get more information, get support himself, and support you in getting help. Alternatively, knowing he can stay with baby so you can do the things you need to care for yourself is also a wonderful gift.

Letter to share with your partner

Dear _____,

One of the biggest shifts a mom faces is suddenly not being able to take care of her basic needs with a baby attached all the time. Many partners simply don't realize this. There are small ways to help lessen any possible frustration or resentment that might build up. Let your partner know that you are here for her, open to hearing what she needs, and that you want to help. If she is really struggling, this may be a good opening for her to talk about it and to come up with a plan for getting support (family, priest, sisterhood, friends) and help (babysitter, cleaning, meal prep, postpartum doula, or professional counseling) as needed. Review the list above with her and see what areas she needs your help in the most, or make a practice of checking in with her daily and offering to help.

Thank you for all you are doing to support your new and growing family right now. This can be a hard time for dads and partners, who may be feeling left out as moms and newborns bond so intensely. Please don't underestimate how incredibly important you are to mom and your baby!

DAY 24

Non-Possessiveness

Letting Go of Stuff

Non-possessiveness is the resignation of cares, life without anxiety, an unencumbered wayfarer, alienation from sorrow, fidelity to the commandments.

—SAINT JOHN CLIMACUS[16]

But how can they follow Christ, who are held back by the chain of their wealth? Or how can they seek heaven, and climb to sublime and lofty heights, who are weighed down by earthly desires? They think that they possess, when they are rather possessed; as slaves of their profit, and not lords with respect to their own money, but rather the bond-slaves of their money.

—SAINT CYPRIAN OF CARTHAGE[17]

---

16 *Ladder*, p. 122.
17 Cyprian of Carthage, *Treatises*, 3:12, accessed March 21, 2021, http://www.newadvent.org/fathers/050703.htm.

It is not difficult to get rid of material things if you so desire; but only with great effort will you be able to get rid of thoughts about them.

—SAINT THALASSIOS THE LIBYAN[18]

For the Soul

After reflecting yesterday on our love of money, we turn our gaze toward what we already have, making sure that our current possessions don't tether us to earthly things when we should focus on being "rich toward God" (Luke 12:21). As Christians we know that we must not allow ourselves to be possessed by our possessions, and yet do we really live that way? Saint Cyprian warns in the quotes above that we are not owners but owned; we are not masters of our money but are enslaved by it.

Many of us don't think we are attached to our things, yet when something breaks or we imagine doing without it, we feel a sense of anxiety or loss. We may even wonder what the harm is in loving our things as long as we love God more. But in Matthew 6:24 we are warned, "No one can serve two masters; for either he will hate the one and love the other, or else he will be loyal to the one and despise the other. You cannot serve God and mammon."[19]

As new parents, we can begin to feel the need for a whole new array of things we never needed before—diapers, baby blankets, high chairs, bottles, pacifiers, toys, etc. There are many things we may want to buy for our babies, and as first-time moms, we truly may not know what we do and do not need. To complicate this situation, there is no shortage of items marketed for infants.

---

18   "On Love," *The Philokalia*, vol. 2, p. 320.

19   *Mammon* roughly translates to "wealth," "riches," or "gain," from the Aramaic term *māmōnā. Encyclopedia Britannica*, https://www.britannica.com/topic/mammon (accessed October 12, 2020).

Baby registries are full of every sort of contraption that one might want to help soothe, carry, feed, clean, and entertain our precious new child. As new parents we are very vulnerable to this targeted advertising. We don't know what we will or won't need, and we have not yet seen the slow and steady flow of stuff that having a child will bring into our lives—not just at baby's birth but with every birthday, holiday, or trip to the store.

Twenty-four days in we may well be mired in this stuff and even beginning to notice our attachment to it. *How can I get him to sleep without that swaddle/white noise machine? How will I know she's safe if I don't have a monitor? Everyone says this baby carrier is the best! We need it!* We might be surprised at how much we have come to rely on things in becoming parents. Does it need to be like this? The beautiful 2010 documentary *Babies* does a wonderful job of showing how basic and uncomplicated life can be with babies around. From experience we can say that less is more, except maybe in terms of diapers and infant outfits—it's shocking how many times a small baby can need to be changed in one day!

So, what, after all, does a baby need more than anything else? Our love. And that takes no wrapping paper. We don't mean to belittle the fact that some things make caring for our baby simpler and perhaps even safer. But we must be intentional about what we allow to come into our lives and homes, especially at this time of transition. Starting at the beginning of our baby's life can save a lot of time and stress in the long run. Each new thing we accumulate requires space and time to maintain and potentially takes our baby out of our hands and away from face-to-face connection.

Making do with less will serve us well and set a good example for our children. Making a choice from the beginning to limit stuff will help to create more space, time, and freedom. In being intentional about what we bring into our home and not becoming attached to all the things we could buy, we are able to let the consumerist push pass us by. Perhaps this freedom will allow us to do less and be more, in stillness and prayer and in communion with our tiny child and God.

SAINT SOPHIA OF THRACE (JUNE 4/17)[20]
Greece, circa AD 700

Saint Sophia is an example of many virtues. She was known for her humility, love, fasting, and great care for orphans and widows. She lived in Thrace, Greece, and was a well-educated woman who married and had six children. In her life as a wife and mother she focused on creating a Christian home for her family.

While she was a model of living a spiritual life as a mother, Sophia endured the tragedy of losing her husband and children in a plague that struck the city. In her unbearable loss, Sophia turned to God for direction for the future course of her life. Over the next twenty years she adopted more than one hundred orphans and raised them as Christians. We can only imagine the love God poured through her heart to these many souls. For this she is known as "the Mother of Orphans."

In her care of those around her, Sophia often went without to make sure others had what was necessary. She is an example of extreme faithfulness to God and trusting that He will provide, even when we can't imagine how we will

---

20 *Marriage as a Path to Holiness*, p. 195.

proceed. We can pray to her for help in letting go of what we don't need and trusting in God's plan for our lives.

For Mind & Body

CHECK-IN

We are just over halfway through our forty days! This is a good time to check in. Are you making time to care for yourself as well as your baby? When you feed your baby, are you remembering to feed yourself? When was the last time you took a shower or had a quick soak in the tub? Are you making time to check in with your partner and/or a friend? This is your gentle reminder to take care of yourself. Just as you might think to check in on a friend who is going through a busy or trying period, we suggest making time regularly to check in with yourself. This is hard to do but very important! Remember, it's for the well-being of your whole family, too. *Our peace brings peace.*

Below are some suggestions for combining self-care and baby care:

» Take a bath while you let baby do some tummy or floor time on a mat in the bathroom. If and when your baby gets fussy, bring her into the tub!

» Do some gentle stretches on the ground while your baby does tummy time on your chest.

» Lay baby naked on a towel. Use some warm coconut oil to massage his arms, legs, chest, and torso while you also give your own tired, possibly still swollen, feet and legs a rub.

» Put baby in a carrier or stroller and go outside for a walk (in a natural setting if you can).

SARAH

I can tell you I didn't do enough checking in during the early days of motherhood. I tried to be superhuman by taking care of every one of my family's needs. This led to exhaustion and resentment. My husband and I had some important conversations that helped me to see he was there to help. I didn't need to prove I could do it all, but I did need to ask for what I needed, as no one around me could read my mind. I also learned how much of an introvert I am and that I am not able to go non-stop all day, every day, with inquisitive kids and constant needs. Keeping naptime and quiet time is critical for all of us, but especially for me—I need a few moments to reset when I can be still without any input or output.

As my kids grow, I am still learning what else I need to do for self-care. It took me a while to realize how crucial daily movement is to my overall ability to remain loving, calm, and happy. Now, I get up early to pray, write, exercise, and take a walk. I regularly call friends and talk with my mother on my walk. This time for connection and taking care of myself refills my cup and enables me to be more present and loving with my family.

PART VI

Further Passions of the Soul

Motherhood is a mirror revealing weaknesses we hadn't been aware of previously but which now stare back at us all obvious and unavoidable. Though it stings, this realization can be a springboard for some serious growth if we can view it as an opportunity to dig deep and weed out the sins which keep us chained to self-centeredness and earthly cares.

—MOLLY SABOURIN[1]

---

1 Molly Sabourin, "Motherhood: Let It Break You but Don't Despair," Orthodox Motherhood, Sept. 14, 2016, http://www.orthodoxmotherhood.com/motherhood/ (accessed July 4, 2020).

DAY 25

Insensibility

Our Blindness to God

Insensibility is negligence that has become habit.

—SAINT JOHN CLIMACUS[2]

To fall into stonelike insensibility is the same as to die; so also to be blind in mind is the same as to lose sight of one's bodily eyes. For he who has fallen into insensibility is deprived of the life-giving forces; and he whose mind is blind is deprived of Divine Light by which a man can see and be seen.

—SAINT GREGORY OF SINAI[3]

The truly intelligent man pursues one sole objective: to obey and conform to the God of all. With this single aim in view, he disciplines his soul, and whatever he may encounter in

---

2   *Ladder*, p. 124.
3   St. Herman of Alaska Brotherhood, *Heavenly Wisdom from God-illumined Teachers on Conquering Depression* (Platina, CA: St. Herman of Alaska Brotherhood, 1995), p. 24.

the course of his life, he gives thanks to God for the com-
pass and depth of His providential ordering of all things.
For it is absurd to be grateful to doctors who give us bitter
and unpleasant medicines to cure our bodies, and yet to be
ungrateful to God for what appears to us to be harsh, not
grasping that all we encounter is for our benefit and in accor-
dance with His providence. For knowledge of God and faith
in Him is the salvation and perfection of the soul.

—SAINT ANTHONY THE GREAT[4]

For the Soul

Sometimes when we are so full of the business and matters of the world, it can be hard to slow down, take moments of pause, and let our heart turn to God. If we stay in this place of external focus, we can slowly dampen the spiritual flame we have inside. As in Jesus' parable of the sower in Matthew 13, we can allow the word of God to fall on stony places or among thorns, or, worse yet, not even be attuned to the word of God.

This passion on St. John's ladder is insensibility to God's life-giving energy and apathy toward the state of our soul. In some translations it is referred to as insensitivity, which we further understand as lacking sensitivity, or keen awareness, to the ways and workings of God. Father Vassilios poignantly describes insensitivity thus: "No matter how much I confess my sin, no matter how guilty I feel, however much I yearn for holiness, I am too lazy and indifferent to go through the arduous struggle holiness demands."[5] For many of us, we may know what we can do to move closer to God, we may even say

---

4 St. Anthony the Great, "On the Character of Men and on the Virtuous Life: One Hundred and Seventy Texts," in *The Philokalia*, vol. 1, p. 329 no. 2.

5 *Thirty Steps to Heaven*, p. 147.

we want it, but we just don't take the time or make the effort.

Being honest with ourselves about this is an important first step. Some of us may yearn to be close to God but actually fear what that would mean. We may fear our own sinfulness. We may fear what sitting in the presence of God will actually be like and be troubled over what we have to let go of to get there. We are happy to go through all the motions, but really letting our hearts be pierced by the all-consuming fire of God's love feels like another thing altogether. We may fear the fact that truly turning toward God means giving up some of what we like and submitting our own will. We may be afraid of what God wants of us, even if we already know deep down what it is.

This is a challenging step on the ladder because it prompts us to look at ourselves in this new light. When we reflect on this passion, we must ask ourselves, "Am I truly sensitive to the things of God in my life? If I am honest with myself, do I put my spiritual life and my relationship with God before all my earthly duties, tasks, and cares?" These are hard questions, and they don't get any easier when we become mothers. As both our responsibilities and time restraints increase, finding the time and energy to devote to our spiritual lives can feel overwhelming, even burdensome at times. If we notice that we feel this way, we can begin by shifting our understanding of how we can be with God.

Our seeking of God should not feel like a burden, for He is the one who can lighten our load. In Matthew 11:28–30 we are told, "Come to Me, all *you* who labor and are heavy laden, and I will give you rest. Take My yoke upon you and learn from Me, for I am gentle and lowly in heart, and you will find rest for your souls. For My yoke *is* easy and My burden is light." When everything feels overwhelming and we are tired and sore, we can retune our thinking from, "Oh, I haven't said my prayers, I am too tired" to "Lord, have mercy on me. Please help Your servant to find strength. Please help me to bear the trials of my day, give me strength to care for my baby into the wee hours, let me feel Your presence in the still moments, and be with me throughout the day and night." We can call upon Him for renewed energy and strength; we can share with Him our worries and fears that seem too great to bear. In this way our faith can be a living faith, a daily, moment-to-moment faith. Just this change of perspective can increase our awareness of God in our heart and all aspects of our life. This is especially important now when we may not be able to fulfill our usual obedience of prayer and liturgical life.

From this place of living faith we begin to cultivate sensitivity toward what God wants from us and for us. The sensitivity we have toward our newborn child beautifully mirrors the sensitivity we must have for God. Our newborn baby's language is unknown to us, and in the earliest days we have yet to learn how to interpret his cries. With time we begin to tune in to the nuances of her movements and sounds, as well as her daily rhythms, likes, and dislikes. We can liken this honing of our intuition to the spiritual radar we use to create connection with God, allowing space for understanding and deciphering His voice in our lives. It is only through time spent together and careful observation that we gain these skills with our child. The same is true of our relationship with God.

SAINT MARTHA (JULY 4/17)[6]

Antioch, Early Sixth Century

Saint Martha had hoped to be a nun, but her parents arranged for her to be married. Before her wedding, St.

---

6   *Marriage as a Path to Holiness*, pp. 207–208.

John the Baptist appeared to her, instructed her to be married, and told her that her child would be a holy man. With this vision to guide her, Martha entered into marriage and proceeded to live a devout and pious life. She dedicated herself to prayer, even rising at midnight to pray, and loved being in church. Saint Martha was known for serving her neighbors by sewing baptismal gowns and burial shrouds to give to those in need. She offered hospitality to strangers, clothed the naked, tended to the sick, and fed those who were hungry. Through her great faith and example, her son grew to know God and later became St. Simeon of the Wonderful Mountain.

Saint Martha is an example of a faithful Christian and mother who remained sensitive to the things of God through her prayer life and care of those around her. We can pray to her to help keep our hearts sensitive to the Lord and to help us follow her example of prayer, humility, and almsgiving.

SARAH

I always thought of myself as a calm, gentle, and even-tempered person. Then I became a mother. Over the years I have been amazed at how quickly I can lose my temper, how outraged I can be, how irrationally I can act over the normal behavior of children testing boundaries and needing attention. Children are children; some can be more difficult than others, but it is the way we as parents respond, love, and support them that will guide them in overcoming these behaviors and developing a strong character.

Saint Porphyrios explains this:

What saves and makes for good children is the life of the parents in the home. The parents need to devote themselves to the love of God. They need to become saints in their relations to their children through their mildness, patience, and love. They need to make a new start every day, with a fresh outlook, renewed enthusiasm and love for their children. And the joy that will come to them, the holiness that will visit them, will shower grace on their children.[7]

Realizing that I am far from a model of virtue is very humbling and a great spiritual teacher. This understanding has helped me to see the truth of St. Porphyrios's words: that my spiritual life sets the tone for my home. This concept holds so much truth that it became one of our golden rules of motherhood. Even though much time has passed since this first awareness, in writing this chapter I realize how insensitive I continue to be and how I struggle to change and to do the things that would help me to grow. These are the things of God. Lord, have mercy on me!

For Mind & Body

POSITIVE SELF-TALK

Our peace brings peace. We observe this in so many aspects of our lives, and one that presents itself to us again and again is the way we talk to ourselves. If this baby is our first child, we may not yet have experienced that she will grow to echo our words. Things we might not even realize we say again and again will surprise us when our baby starts talking and we hear, "Just

---

7   Elder Porphyrios, *Wounded by Love: The Life and Wisdom of Elder Porphyrios*, John Raffan, trans. (Evia, Greece: Denise Harvey, 2005), p. 196.

two minutes," "Careful!" "Ouch, don't touch!" or "I love you so much!"

It can be a joy or a moment of chastening to hear our words from our baby's mouth. We may not realize that it is not only our spoken words that our children observe and try out; they also pick up on our internal talk. Our children can sense our mood and understand far more about us than what we tell them in words.

This internal voice, often referred to as self-talk, is the way we speak to ourselves and the running dialogue we keep in our head. Most of us tend to be harder on ourselves than we are on others. While we may intend this to help us change for the better, it is often counterproductive and makes us feel worse. Adults, like children, often act badly when they feel bad. For example, at moments of struggle or disappointment we might say to ourselves, *I messed up putting the diaper on again. I can't do anything right!* or *I'm so tired, I can barely get to anything; I'm so lazy right now,* or even *She's still crying. She's always crying. I'm a terrible mother!* If we begin to pay attention, we may find we are saying these types of disparaging things to ourselves all day long. Negative self-talk takes a toll on us and can affect our mood, our belief in ourselves, and ultimately our relationship with God.

If we are intentional about how we speak to ourselves, those same moments might sound very different inside our heads: *I'm really getting the hang of this diaper changing thing! Only two ruined outfits today,* or *I know I didn't get to half of what I hoped to do today, but that's okay. I needed my rest and tomorrow is a new day.* We can even use positive self-talk out loud with our baby: "Oh, I'm trying so hard to soothe you and you're still crying. This is hard for both of us! I'll hold you and you can cry. I'm here."

We encourage you to listen to what you say to yourself throughout the day. How do you talk to yourself? With love, forgiveness, and compassion? With hope for growth and confidence in your ability to change and learn? These are important questions for us as mothers to ask ourselves. The voice we use with ourselves often becomes the voice we use for our children. We may even notice, if we pay attention, that this voice is the voice our parents used with us. Talking to ourselves with love and kindness will not only help us forgive and be loving with ourselves; it will also help us model forgiveness and love for our children and, through them, their children for generations to come. Respecting and loving ourselves as fallen children of God, temples of the Holy Spirit who are always deserving of love and forgiveness is a vital step in being able to transmit a sense of God's unlimited love and forgiveness to our children. It also has the potential to completely change the way we view ourselves, our lives, and the many blessings we have been given. The practice below can help us to begin this process.

➤ PRACTICE ◄

Words of Grace

To help with positive self-talk, we can write down statements to keep in mind when we need them. Take a few minutes today to write down three positive statements to remember when you find your thinking going down a negative path. We are not talking about false positivity but words of grace that can bring us comfort in times of need. Even when we might not feel these things in the moment, we know that they are true overall. Some examples are:

» I am doing my best, and that will be enough.

» I am a strong woman, even when I feel weak.

» Darkness may come, but I am filled with the light of Christ.

» Everyone makes mistakes.

» I am a good mother.

» I am grateful for my child.

» I am the mother my baby needs.

If we truly have trouble finding something positive to say to ourselves, it may be a sign of depression, and we should consider getting help (see page 173). In these times, we can always say "The Lord, my God, loves me always," which is true for each and every one of us.

SARAH

Shortly after my third daughter was born, we were having a chaotic moment in the house. The baby was crying, my two older children were running around, and dinner was burning. My mother had just joined us, and I said, "I can't handle this. I can't do all this."

When things settled she turned to me and said, "Honey, I don't think you should say that in front of the children. It is hard and you are stressed, but you can handle it. You can say instead, 'This is so hard. I'm struggling, but I will get through it.' You are strong and your children want to trust that."

Her words struck me because they were true. My children are watching and hearing me, even when I am not speaking to them. If I can model a healthy way of handling stress, they will learn from my example.

DAY 26

Sleep, Prayer, and Church

Bringing Our Children to Church

He who reckons with feeling of heart that he stands before God in prayer shall be an unshakeable pillar.

—SAINT JOHN CLIMACUS[8]

But Jesus said, "Let the little children come to Me, and do not forbid them; for of such is the kingdom of heaven."

—MATTHEW 19:14

And these words which I command you today shall be in your heart. You shall teach them diligently to your children, and shall talk of them when you sit in your house, when you walk by the way, when you lie down, and when you rise up. You shall bind them as a sign on your hand, and they shall be as frontlets between your eyes. You shall write them on the doorposts of your house and on your gates.

—DEUTERONOMY 6:6–9

---

8   *Ladder*, pp. 127–128.

When your children are still small, you have to help them understand what is good. That is the deepest meaning of life.

—SAINT PAISIOS[9]

For the Soul

Although it may yet feel a long way off, you will soon bring this new little bundle into the fold of your parish. We aren't going to pretend that bringing children to church is always easy. There are many services when we've wanted to cry in the corner because our children were loud or ran across the nave, or we felt judgmental eyes staring at our unsuccessful efforts to rein in unruly toddlers. Having gotten through this time with some of our older children has shown us that our efforts are not fruitless. Watching our children light candles, cross themselves, kiss the icons, and sing along with the choir are some of the joyous fruits of bringing our children to church.

Still, we may wonder how we can bring an infant to church. Shouldn't we wait until he is older and can focus? What if she cries? These of course can be difficult moments, and some parishes are more welcoming to children than others. But truly, if a parish does not have young voices, who will grow up to keep the church alive?

Being in an Orthodox church is profoundly experiential—the smell of incense, the sight of flickering candles and icons, the sound of chanting, and the taste of Holy Communion. These sensory experiences are meaningful to our children well before they are able to understand the significance of the prayers or church customs. When our children are infants, they are open to the love

---

9   http://www.orthodoxchurchquotes.com/2014/07/18/elder-paisios-when-your-children-are-still-small/ (accessed Sept. 2, 2020).

of God in a way that we as adults may not understand. Simply being in church and witnessing the services brings these experiences into our children's hearts and inner consciousness. By bringing our children to church, we help them feel at home in God's house. We instill the love of His services in their hearts and allow them a taste of the grace they can find there.

⁓

Train up a child in the way he should go,
And when he is old he will not depart from it.

—PROVERBS 22:6

⁓

Being in church with our children also allows *us* to grow spiritually. This may not happen in the way we planned, as it can be very hard to focus on our own prayers and spiritual state when attending to children, especially if we fear disrupting the worship of fellow parishioners. Elissa Bjeletich in her *Raising Saints* podcast said, "Sometimes we think that our kids get in the way of our faith, not noticing that they are the place where we work out our faith. We aren't spiritually lacking because we're too busy dealing with the family; they are the struggles that God has sent so that we can build up our spiritual lives."[10] *Use the struggle to grow in faith and love.*

Our children offer so much spiritual food, opportunity for growth, and unconditional love. In church they offer plenty of practice in patience and delaying our own gratification while we support their spiritual growth and development. As they grow, they may also prompt us to be intentional about our faith in a way we were not before.

---

10   "Parenting," *Raising Saints.*

~

A mother's prayers are the cries and laughs of her children.

—ORTHODOX MOTHER

~

Through bringing our children to church we learn perseverance, patience, humility, and how to be part of the Body of Christ. Saint Porphyrios writes, "The important thing is for us to enter into the Church—to unite ourselves with our fellow men, with the joys and sorrows of each and every one, to feel that they are our own, to pray for everyone, to have a care for their salvation, to forget about ourselves. To do everything for them just as Christ did for us."[11] Being in church teaches us how to be Christians: we take upon ourselves the joy, the pain, and the burdens of one another as we are united in love as the Body of Christ. Sometimes this means that *we* are burdensome, and this can allow others to care for us, to hold our babies in church, to take older siblings to light candles, to delight in our baby's baptism and communion with us. What a gift for us to bring our children in their infancy and show them the love of the Lord and His house from their earliest days.

SASHA

The parish I grew up in and still attend today currently has very few small children. Many Sundays my children are the only little ones there. I often feel self-conscious and worried that they are the only little ones running about or making a fuss. I remember clearly, before I had children, being quite judgmental about how distracting young children could be in church. May God forgive me for this. Many of

---

11   *Wounded by Love*, p. 88.

those same judgments come into my mind in church, and I assume others find us equally disruptive.

Early on in motherhood I shared this with Sarah, and she reminded me that children are the future of our church. So many moments I find myself working hard to temper my self-consciousness so that my children won't feel that church is a place they are unwelcome—constantly shushed and scolded. Instead I try to engage them as much as possible, lighting candles or helping to put them out, swinging the lanterns before certain hymns, helping them memorize the different saints' names and whispering translations of supplicatory prayers into their ears. Sometimes they color pictures of the saints and read church-themed board books. I work hard each service to keep my children in church and engaged, disturbing others as little as possible.

In each service I also make sure I have five or ten minutes of uninterrupted prayer time for myself—sometimes during the pre-communion or thanksgiving prayers. My church prayer is nothing compared to that of my pre-child life—and yet, I have grown spiritually a hundredfold since having children, and I know that God blesses my efforts. By His grace, in each service I am still granted a taste of that peace that surpasses all understanding. I pray my children also drink from the fountain of God's love that will nourish and sustain them all their lives.

For Mind & Body

SLEEP

Sleep is one of the most elusive goals of early motherhood. There is no way to prepare for the bone-deep tiredness, foggy brain, and crushing weight of exhaustion the multiple night wakings of infancy can bring. Having a helping hand goes a long way, but many of us will find that we are the sole night caretakers and are left wondering how we can get through it.

In her book *Fertile Ground*, Orthodox doula and writer Laura Jansson uses the term "nighttime ministry"[12] to describe this time at night with our babies. This phrase captures the essence of this time and how we can conceptualize it for our own growth and offering of love to our baby. *Use the struggle to grow in faith and love.* We call upon the depth of our love to rise in the night to rock, kiss, hold, change, and feed our helpless baby, when all we want to do is roll back over and close our eyes. This is our ministry. This is our call from God in these moments. Thinking of this time as a ministry will go a long way toward buoying our strength and helping us recognize the importance of our work.

As beautiful as this ministry is, it is hard. Lack of sleep can cause tearfulness, frustration, and general difficulty coping. Good self-care includes helping our baby to sleep. This is important for us, but it is also very important for our baby, whose neurological system relies on periods of extended sleep, when possible, to re-equilibrate and integrate information collected throughout wakeful periods. Each baby is different, and babies' sleep patterns vary tremendously. But starting with a regular routine early on can help the whole family sleep better.

A gentle pre-bed routine can set the stage and help baby recognize the start of nighttime sleep. Simply preparing baby for bed by doing the same combination of activities (e.g., baby massage, water-only bath, changing, singing, feeding, prayer, rocking) can help baby develop good sleep associations.

While many of us may worry that we do things that create

---

12   *Fertile Ground*, p. 228.

unhealthy long-term sleep associations (e.g., letting baby fall asleep on the breast or in our arms), many babies at this young age will not be able to fall asleep on their own. If your baby can fall asleep on her own this young, by all means let her. This will make life easier later on. However, for the rest of us, while there will be a time and place for helping baby learn to fall asleep without us, these first forty days are likely not the time. For more help with baby sleep, see our favorite suggestions in the Resources section on page 369.

➤ PRACTICE ◄

Evening Routine for Mom

The days and nights may still be blurring into one another, but you are likely starting to see patterns and routines developing. As we describe above, creating a wind-down and sleep routine for your child is an important step in building good sleep habits. We believe the same is true for ourselves. As you have more time and energy, you can add to your own routine. If you already have one established that works well, keep going! A good basic routine can take as little as five minutes and can make a big difference. These same strategies can help in the middle of the night if you find you are awake with worries or restlessness.

Some Ideas for a Basic Evening Routine
Prepare your body and space for sleep. To help your body begin to wind down, consider the hour before you hope to fall asleep protected time. To aid your natural circadian rhythm, try to have a set time for going to bed and keep the lights low. Likely baby is nearby, so consider lighting that will not be too

disruptive but will allow you to write or read quietly for a few minutes. We like a dimmable light by the head of the bed or LED candles. Ideally, avoid looking at screens for the hour before sleep. Wear clothing with layers as your hormones can make you heat up. A cozy pair of socks and/or a hot water bottle can be helpful for getting to sleep on colder nights. Make sure you have a glass of water nearby along with anything you will need to care for baby during the night—burp cloths, a diaper, wipes, and a change of clothes. Finally, having a warm cup of chamomile tea or other herbal tea you enjoy can be a nice pre-bed ritual.

Formal prayer. During the early and largely sleepless days with a newborn, rather than abandoning formal prayer altogether, consider choosing one or two prayers that you feel would be most helpful and fruitful for you during this time and keeping them printed up by your bedside.

Informal prayer/journaling. Taking a few moments to write in your journal before bed can help you clear your mind and unburden yourself before sleep. Consider writing a letter to God or the Theotokos—include your daily gratitude practice and your worries about failings or struggles. End by asking for whatever you feel you need right now to help make tomorrow a better day. You can use this space to write down to-dos as well or things you want to remember to address the next day. This space is for you. If writing feels too difficult, consider the practice described on page 139 of prayer to the Theotokos.

Reading. For some, reading can be an excellent way to disconnect our brains from our own worries and thoughts, which is ultimately what we must do to fall asleep. Consider reading from Scripture or something spiritual and uplifting.

Quiet moment of stillness and breathing. You can start or end your wind down with some intentional breathing. Sometimes taking a few breaths as you get into bed can set you up better for prayer and/or journaling; or you may find it more helpful to do this just as you are getting ready to drift off. Either way, consider spending a few minutes sitting or lying quietly and focusing on the simple movement of your breath. You can connect the breath with an arrow prayer or the Jesus prayer as in the exercise on page 68. Intentional breathing can help to bring a sense of calm, activating your parasympathetic nervous system and preparing your mind and body for sleep.

Alertness

Keeping Our Own Vigil

A vigilant eye makes the mind pure.

—SAINT JOHN CLIMACUS[13]

If you think of the number of empty minutes in a day when we will be doing something because we are afraid of emptiness and of being alone with ourselves, you will realise that there are plenty of short periods which could belong both to us and to God at the same time.

—METROPOLITAN ANTHONY OF SOUROZH[14]

This is the aim of the enemy of the human race, the devil: to continually sift us like wheat, forcing us to constantly spin in the whirlwind of entertainments and diversions, not allowing

---

13   *Ladder*, p. 128.
14   Anthony Bloom, *Beginning to Pray* (London: Darton, Longman & Todd, 1970), p. 81.

us to collect ourselves and contemplate our inner state, our soul.

—ARCHBISHOP AVERKY (TAUSHEV)[15]

For the Soul

This step on St. John's ladder was originally intended to offer instruction on the monastic tradition of the all-night vigil. This is not something laypeople, especially new mothers, are expected to do; however, this does not mean that the virtue of alertness has nothing to do with us.

The word *vigil* originated from the Latin *vigilia,* meaning "wakefulness." It can be defined as "the act of keeping awake when sleep is customary."[16] As Christians, we are all called to be in constant spiritual devotion and watchfulness, as we are cautioned in Matthew 24:42–44:

Watch therefore, for you do not know what hour your Lord is coming. But know this, that if the master of the house had known what hour the thief would come, he would have watched and not allowed his house to be broken into. Therefore you also be ready, for the Son of Man is coming at an hour you do not expect.

As new mothers we may have more in common with this concept of keeping vigil than we realize. With a tiny newborn in our care, we are on twenty-four-hour alert, waking up throughout the night to keep watch and tend to the needs of our newborn. This same

---

15   Archbishop Averky, *The Struggle for Virtue: Asceticism in a Modern Secular Society* (Jordanville, NY: The Printshop of St. Job of Pochaev, 2014), p. 96.

16   "Vigil," Merriam-Webster.com, accessed June 30, 2020, https://www.merriam-webster.com/dictionary/vigil.

kind of attention, when turned toward the things of God, is the meaning of alertness in our spiritual lives. If, while caring for tiny babies, we allow our minds and hours to be filled with distractions and other activities, we may miss the subtle but important cues of hunger or fatigue and end up with a very unhappy baby. In our relationship with God, it is instead we who suffer when we miss the ways in which He is trying to connect with us and guide us.

A couple of days ago, looking at the vice of insensibility, we recognized our need to develop our spiritual radar. Today we focus on all the clutter that interferes with our ability to follow our radar or even remember there is a radar to follow. There are so many distractions around us in addition to the many things we need to do to live, function, and take care of the tiny being(s) in our care. We must seek a balanced course. One key to this is being intentional in setting priorities and staying connected with them. In keeping our own vigil we must make sure that our relationship with God is always at the top of our to-do list. Saint Paul defines where our focus should be:

Finally, brethren, whatever things are true, whatever things are noble, whatever things are just, whatever things are pure, whatever things are lovely, whatever things are of good report, if there is any virtue and if there is anything praiseworthy— meditate on these things. (Phil. 4:8)

Our days take on a different rhythm in these first weeks and months. Often space is created in the middle of the night, or when others are at work or school, that we may be tempted to fill with distractions. We all have our own particular distractions that we love—television, magazines, shopping, social media, you name it. Technology has brought a whole slew of tantalizing distractions that are so easy to indulge in while we are nursing or awake at night. We may think of these things as simple pastimes, but it is important to remember that they can take up significant portions of the precious time we have been given. Unless we are intentional about where and when we allow time for these things, they can quietly begin to take over our lives.

In being intentional, we can focus on many aspects of the entertainment we consume, specifically what and how much. Especially in these early days, not only the quantity but also the quality of what fills our time is important to consider. New mothers are flooded with hormones and worries. We should be gentle with ourselves and recognize how sensitive and impressionable we are right now. Much of what is available to watch is intended to excite, shock, and stimulate. Even children's films are often filled with frightening and intense imagery. When we stop to think that we are taking these words, sounds, and images into our hearts and minds, it can give us pause. Unwholesome programming is so ubiquitous, many of us become desensitized to images and themes that are quite dark. The same can be said of print media with their photos of models and picture-perfect families, and of social media, where everyone is posting the most idealized versions of their own lives and accomplishments. The likelihood is that too much time with any of these distractions will leave us feeling empty or, worse, despondent and agitated.

It is worth remembering that these technology-based, advertisement-supported outlets have been created by people who are trained to get our attention and keep it. James Williams, a former Google advertising strategist turned philosopher, wrote an eye-opening book called *Stand Out of Our Light*. In it he discusses humanity's choice to give our attention over to media-driven consumerism, in which the world's best mathematicians, economists, and artists are employed to capture our attention as we slowly give over our will.[17] If we are not careful, and if we don't set limits, it is all too easy to flit from one thing to the next and spend hours on really nothing at all.

C. S. Lewis's book *The Screwtape Letters,* written as if from a master demon instructing a minor demon on how to steal the soul of his "patient," describes this phenomenon in a provocative way:

> *All the healthy and out-going activities which we want him to avoid can be inhibited and nothing given in return, so that at least he may say, as one of my own patients said on his arrival down here, 'I now see that I spent most of my life in doing neither what I ought nor what I liked.' The Christians describe the Enemy as one 'without whom Nothing is strong.' And Nothing is very strong: strong enough to steal away a man's best years not in sweet sins but in a dreary flickering of the mind over it knows not what and knows not why. . . . It does not matter how small the sins are provided that their cumulative effect is to edge the man away from the Light and out into the Nothing. Murder is no better than cards if cards can do the trick.[18]*

The truth is if we are not intentional, the choices will be made for us. Even in these early days we have a choice of how to fill our time and what will fill us. These first forty days will never be ours again; it is well worth considering how to use them to create a special space for our spiritual selves and emotions. We are precious

---

17 James Williams, *Stand Out of Our Light: Freedom and Resistance in the Attention Economy* (Cambridge, UK: Cambridge University Press, 2018).

18 C. S. Lewis, *The Screwtape Letters* (New York: HarperCollins, 2001), pp. 60–61.

in the sight of the Lord, as our children are precious to us. Caring for ourselves in this way is an act of love. We strongly suggest for the sake of your soul and the souls of your children that you use media sparingly, with awareness and attention, and shield your children from screens and tablets as long as you can. The American Academy of Pediatrics recommends no independent screen time before two years of age and strictly limited time thereafter.[19] While the issues with children's screen time are beyond the scope of this book, we can recognize that our own screen time and intentionality will be one of the main factors influencing our children's future media use.

For Mind & Body

MINDFUL TECHNOLOGY USE

The next time you are out in public or in your home with others and find yourself looking at your phone, pause and note how long you were focused on your phone. Was it one minute? Five minutes? Ten? Did more time pass than you realized? What were the other people around you doing while you were "away"? Were they also using devices? What is your baby doing when you are looking at a screen? Take a minute to notice people around you now. Are they aware you are available now? Are you making eye contact with anyone? Practicing this awareness regularly can help us to see whether and how much we are losing by getting lost in our devices. It can help make us more open to what is happening in front of us.

---

19 American Academy of Pediatrics, *Where we stand: screen time*, https://www.healthychildren.org/English/family-life/Media/Pages/Where-We-Stand-TV-Viewing-Time.aspx (accessed March 27, 2021).

SARAH

Once I was playing with my baby and got a message on my phone. As I checked my phone, I saw another notification and soon was swept into a rabbit hole of Facebook posts. I came back to reality a few minutes later, and my daughter was just looking at me. It was a moment of realization. During the time I was totally occupied and in my own world, my daughter was waiting patiently for me. I've noticed many times since, especially as I've tried to cut down on my own phone use around others, that I will be with someone or in a public space, and people will disappear into their devices, unaware that the rest of us are still present.

Now I try to be aware of how often I use my phone in front of my children. I restrict lengthy reads or time on social media to times when I am alone or after they are asleep. I often keep my phone far from me during the day so that I am not attuned to it and constantly being pulled away by texts or emails.

DAY 28

Fear

Letting Our Faith Be Bigger Than Our Fear

He who has become the servant of the Lord will fear his Master alone, but he who does not yet fear Him is often afraid of his own shadow.

—SAINT JOHN CLIMACUS[20]

Filled with love, the holy Apostles went into the world, preaching salvation to mankind and fearing nothing, for the Spirit of God was their strength. When St. Andrew was threatened with death upon the cross if he did not stay his preaching he answered: "If I feared the cross I should not be preaching the Cross." In this manner all the other Apostles, and after them the martyrs and holy men who wrestled against evil, went forward with joy to meet pain and suffering. For the Holy Spirit, sweet and gracious, draws the soul to love the Lord,

---

20   *Ladder*, p. 1.

*and in the sweetness of the Holy Spirit the soul loses her fear
of suffering.*

—SAINT SILOUAN THE ATHONITE[21]

*But now, thus says the LORD, who created you, O Jacob,
And He who formed you, O Israel:
"Fear not, for I have redeemed you;
I have called you by your name;
You are Mine.
When you pass through the waters, I will be with you;
And through the rivers, they shall not overflow you.
When you walk through the fire, you shall not be burned,
Nor shall the flame scorch you.
For I am the LORD your God, . . .
Since you were precious in My sight,
You have been honored,
And I have loved you; . . .
Fear not, for I am with you."*

—ISAIAH 43:1–5

For the Soul

Let us take heart and hear these words from Isaiah once again:
"You were precious in My sight . . . And I have loved you . . .
Fear not, for I am with you." This is the promise of our God. We
are loved, we are precious, and we are not alone. Whatever comes
our way, He will care for us. He says this to each and every one
of us and to our child(ren) too. Today there may be no big scary
monsters lurking in the closet. Our hope is that you are peacefully

---

21 Archimandrite Sophrony, *Wisdom from Mount Athos: The Writings of
Staretz Silouan, 1866–1938,* trans. Rosemary Edmonds (Crestwood, NY: St.
Vladimir's Seminary Press, 1974).

reading, your heart full of love, your belly full of good food, and your sleeping baby near. But we know how easy it is for fear to creep into our hearts, especially in these early days when we feel so vulnerable and our baby is so helpless.

In pre-pandemic times, over 24 million people visited one of America's Six Flags theme parks each year.[22] Seeking thrills and daring adventure, people ride the Judge Roy Scream, the Dive Devil, and the Apocalypse to get their hearts racing while enduring terrifying speeds and free falls. Why do they ride again and again? Why are they not afraid? The key element here, between thrill and fear, is *trust*. The riders trust that they are not in true danger, that each ride has a safety net that will protect them.

When daily life throws us its own thrills, when fear finds its way into our hearts, we need to remember *our* steadfast safety net. Trust is a crucial part of our relationship with God. In living through the trials of our lives, we pray to understand "that all things work together for good to those who love God" (Romans 8:28). As Christians, we pray to have faith in His Providence, that He will keep us safe, and when calamity does befall us, that He will walk with us along the way, and through Him we will overcome.

~

There is no fear in love; but perfect love casts out fear.

—1 JOHN 4:18

~

As mothers, we pray to grow in courage as we head into this era with a new life. With the sword and shield of the Lord at our

---

22   Eric Platt and Matthew Boesler, "7 Fascinating Facts About Six Flags," *Business Insider*, Jul 23, 2012, https://www.businessinsider.com/six-flags-facts-2012-7 (Accessed Jan. 9, 2020).

breast, with faith guiding us and His love to shine light in the dark, scary places, we go forth. This trust, our faith in God, is a primary support for us as mothers. *We are in God's hands.* Our faith will strengthen us and our whole family. It is a pervasive strength that will calm our fears and daily anxieties and support our whole household. If we can tap into this strength given from the Lord, our fear will shrink. We may discover a deep underlying sense of capability and a reliance on God, allowing us to take heart and know that we are cared for by a Good Shepherd who will strengthen us for all that will come our way.

✝ PRAYER: PSALM 23 (KJV) ✝

One of the most beloved Psalms, Psalm 23, is a true comfort to say in moments when fear and doubt flood our minds. This is a wonderful prayer, especially when we need extra strength and a reminder to give our fear to the Lord. It is worth printing a copy and keeping somewhere to learn by heart.

A PSALM OF KING DAVID

The Lord is my shepherd; I shall not want.

He maketh me to lie down in green pastures: he leadeth me beside the still waters.

He restoreth my soul: he leadeth me in the paths of righteousness for his name's sake.

Yea, though I walk through the valley of the shadow of death, I will fear no evil: for thou art with me; thy rod and thy staff they comfort me.

Thou preparest a table before me in the presence of mine enemies: thou anointest my head with oil; my cup runneth over.

Surely goodness and mercy shall follow me all the days of my life: and I will dwell in the house of the Lord forever.

SARAH

In the last weeks of my third pregnancy I was very down-trodden. My pregnancy was difficult, my body was large, and each evening my back felt as if it would break. I did not do well in taking my suffering joyfully and felt fear and dread that I would be too weak to give birth. As with my other births, I passed my due date, and when I was a week overdue, I had a difficult checkup with one of my midwives. I left the appointment discouraged and took the rare alone time to go pick up a few things we needed. At the store checkout line I saw a decorative sign that said "Let your faith be bigger than your fear." The words hit me in the gut, then in the heart, and I started to cry. I had spent so much of my pregnancy fighting and afraid of the pain and the physical suffering that I had allowed fear to obscure my strength: my faith that the Lord was by my side, and that I was a strong, capable woman who knew how to birth her baby.

That moment was a turning point for me, a renewal of my reliance on God and a rekindling of my trust in His prov-idence. I increased my prayers, propped that sign where I would see it every day, and went forward to give birth with a new strength. I feel that my suffering and the fear I held led me to that low place where I had to make a choice. Again and again I have to make the choice to lead with courage and with faith that God is above all. Whatever comes, "I will fear no evil, for Thou art with me" (Psalm 23:4).

The fear of the Lord is the beginning of wisdom;
A good understanding have all those who do His
commandments.
His praise endures forever.

—PSALM 111:10

~

For Mind & Body

CORE STRENGTH AND PELVIC HEALTH

From the strength of our faith, we now turn to the strength of our bodies. During pregnancy our bodies go through so much, and we are often humbled by the changes. After pregnancy and birth our backs are prone to tension and soreness from the demands of caring for and holding a baby. Our pelvic floor muscles (the muscles that hold things up when we sneeze) stretch and weaken as our belly grows and during birth. Many first-time mothers are quite surprised to find that the muscles of their belly and pelvic region feel unrecognizable after birth. Shortly after giving birth to a baby, few of us can consciously connect with or control these muscles.

To help rebuild your muscles and prevent pain and incontinence down the road, it can be helpful to practice strengthening exercises. Below is a list of exercises to help you heal and regain strength. Please only do the ones that you are able to do without any strain or pain. These exercises can be done daily or as often as you remember. Listen to an audio version of this and the other exercises in the book on our podcast, *A Sacred Beginning*, on ancientfaith.com.

Exercises for Back and Pelvic Health

Kegels: While sitting or lying down, contract the muscles of your vagina and perineum. You can help locate these muscles by thinking about trying to hold your urine. As you contract the muscles, think of lifting them up and into your body. Hold for five seconds and then slowly release. Rest for five seconds between repetitions. Slowly work your way up to holding for fifteen seconds at a time.

Core bracing: Lying on your back, inhale, and as you exhale, keep your back on the floor while contracting all the muscles of your core (abdomen, lower back, and mid back) as if you were bracing for impact. Hold for ten seconds. Don't forget to breathe as you do this. Repeat five times.

Pelvic curls: Lie on your back with your knees bent and your feet on the floor. Take a breath in, and as you exhale the breath all the way out, contract your abdominal muscles and slowly curl your hips forward toward your belly. This is a very small movement; your hips should barely leave the ground. Inhale, then slowly exhale, releasing your muscles. When your hips are released, gently press your lower back and sacrum into the floor, giving them a gentle release and counter-stretch. Another way to visualize that is to imagine drawing your belly button down toward your spine. Repeat five times, resting for ten seconds between repetitions.

Back and core release: Start on your hands and knees. Hands should be aligned hip-width apart under your shoulders, and knees should be directly under your hips. Start with a neutral flat back, neck in line with the rest of the spine, gazing at the floor. Gently breathe here, feeling the strength of your back and abdominal muscles engaging. Very slowly, on the in breath, begin to release your belly toward the floor as you lift your gaze and draw your chest forward between your arms. On the out breath, slowly round your mid back up toward the ceiling as you let your chin tuck into your chest and press away from the floor. Repeat this exercise three times, slowly, moving with the breath. If comfortable, come down onto your forearms and repeat this practice with your forearms on the floor. This lower position helps to open up the upper back, a great relief from constantly holding a baby—especially if you're breastfeeding.

Vainglory

The Early Bloom of Pride

The sun shines on all alike, and vainglory beams on all activities. For instance, I am vainglorious when I fast; and when I relax the fast in order to be unnoticed, I am again vainglorious over my prudence. When well-dressed I am quite overcome by vainglory, and when I put on poor clothes I am vainglorious again. When I talk I am defeated, and when I am silent I am again defeated by it. . . . A vainglorious person is a believing idolater; he apparently honors God, but he wants to please not God but men.

—SAINT JOHN CLIMACUS[23]

Abba Nisterus the Great was walking in the desert with a brother. They saw a dragon and they ran away. The brother said to him, "Were you frightened too, Father?" The old man

---

23   *Ladder*, p. 133.

*said to him, "I am not afraid, my child, but it is better for me
to flee, so as not to have to flee from the spirit of vainglory."*[24]

*All of us suffer more often than not, more or less, from van-
ity and pride. And nothing hinders progress in the spiritual
life like these passions. Wherever there is indignation, or dis-
agreement, or dissent—if you look carefully it will turn out
that the greatest part to blame for this is love of praise, and
haughtiness.*

—SAINT AMBROSE[25]

For the Soul

The last two passions on the ladder, vainglory and pride, are
considered by St. John as "the beginning and sum of the passions," which he defines as "unholy self-esteem."[26] Put simply,
vainglory is our desire to be praised; it flatters us into an inflated
view of our merits. We haughtily believe the favor we receive is
due to our own merit, forgetting that our admirable qualities are
gifts that reflect the glory of God.

Vainglory is a concept that can be hard to untangle from
pride. We may be more familiar with the passion of vainglory by
its modern-day name, *vanity*. Perhaps Jane Austen explained it
best in *Pride and Prejudice*: "Pride relates more to our opinion
of ourselves, vanity to what we would have others think of us."[27]
We may want others to view us positively and find us capable or

---

24   Benedicta Ward, *The Sayings of the Desert Fathers: The Alphabetical Collec-
     tion* (Collegeville, MN: Liturgical Press, 1984), pp. 153–155.

25   Olga Rozhneva, "Pride, Vanity, and Self-Esteem. From the Legacy of the
     Optina Elders," Orthodox Christianity, accessed July 8, 2020, https://
     orthochristian.com/71829.html.

26   *Ladder*, p. 132.

27   Jane Austen, *Pride and Prejudice* (London: Penguin Group, 1996), p. 20.

attractive. We may even be pleased with someone being envious of us. This is the stirring of vainglory that can cause us much difficulty, especially as it takes root in our soul and flourishes into the fruited tree of pride.

In new motherhood, we may not be feeling vain about our appearance—often the opposite if we catch a glimpse in the mirror and see spit-up on our shirt and the evidence of a sleepless night shadowing our eyes. We may find that motherhood both feeds and stifles this passion. We are humbled in body by our night ministry and parental vigil, and yet we may crave accolades and acknowledgment that we are doing a good job, that our children are adorable, that we are handling all this so well. A desire for reassurance that we are capable is understandable, as is delighting with others in the gift of our child. Yet we should not expect perfection from ourselves in this delicate time. We can be aware of our own outward striving for praise as we pray within our hearts for God's grace and compassion.

When we become mothers, our lives change rapidly. The person we were may seem very different from the person we are now waking up to every day. Our identities shift, and we may be trying to find our footing and figure out who we are in this new space. Physically, many of us have been greatly changed by pregnancy and childbirth; we may not outwardly be who we were one year ago. Emotionally, we are often not at our best, likely crying easily, overtired, and irritable.

We all know mothers who appear to weather these changes with grace and ease. However, many of us do not, but we may be trying our best to appear as if we do. We may even appear to others to be one of those grace-filled mothers, but is this *our* truth? How are we managing with the lack of sleep and the new chaos of our lives? Do we cry when we want to be joyous? Do we get angry when we wish we could be calm? Do we snap at our partner or belittle ourselves when we want to be filled with love and compassion? Do we sometimes fall into despair while we wish our faith were stronger? And—importantly—are we able to be honest with anyone else about all these things that are happening?

These questions are born from our, the authors', own experience of how humbling and trying this time can be. If we can be honest with ourselves and others, these difficulties of motherhood will allow our humility to grow and temper our vainglory and pride. *Use the struggle to grow in faith and love.*

We may, thanks be to God, have moments when we feel things are going really well—moments when we are graced with patience or compassion or faithfulness. This can also be a place where vainglory lurks. Instead, in these moments when we feel good, capable, and competent, we can thank God for His mercy. Mothering is a humbling process that gives us many opportunities for gratitude. We can be grateful for our growth and praise the Lord, knowing that it is He who gives us grace.

SASHA

Since researching and writing this chapter, I have become more aware of the many and subtle ways that vainglory is present in my life. While this is difficult and painful, I do think it is a blessing—a constant reminder of my fallen nature. I subscribe to a daily Orthodox quote email. One day when I was working on this chapter, I opened my email to read a chastening quote from *How to Live a Holy Life* by Metropolitan Gregory of St. Petersburg: "When you perceive in yourself something worthy of praise, and you feel a desire to tell others about it, try immediately to destroy this desire with the thought that you will not receive any benefit from relating it, but only harm." And so even in the writing of this book, as if I had anything important to say or to contribute, there is vainglory in mentioning that, and also vainglory in suggesting I do not.

In high school I was able to hear a well-known poet speak. I remember most vividly her saying something like "Writing is simply telling others what it is like for you to live." It seemed so simple and true at the time, and it still does. So I pray to God that He will guide Sarah and me in writing our truths—our naked truths—in the hopes that they may bring comfort and even hope to others who are also trying, falling, trying, falling, and always, by God's grace, getting up again.

For Mind & Body

DAILY HUMILITY

As parents we watch our children begin to make mistakes and struggle with their own imperfections—some with more grace and flexibility and some with less. We are just the same. None of us likes to be wrong. Perhaps all we have done in growing up is to learn to be a little more private about our disappointment. This also means we may be more private about our failings and possibly even take less time to reflect and learn from them.

There is a lovely practice in the *Positive Discipline* series by child psychologist Dr. Jane Nelson which recommends each member of the family take a moment to review the mistakes made, and perhaps a lesson learned, openly at the dinner table each day. This same type of practice can also be incorporated into family evening prayers. We can share sins and shortcomings in front of our partner and, eventually, our children as they grow and understand the practice. We can conclude by asking one another for forgiveness and giving thanks for the growth and lessons our failings can offer us. This practice teaches us many of the important virtues we encounter along the ladder, including humility, honesty, patience (as we notice our perennial sins coming up again and again), alertness, and discernment, while building in a daily moment for reflection and outward repentance.

SASHA

I enjoy doing this practice with my oldest child, especially as he struggles greatly when he isn't able to do something perfectly. Each night we review one thing we did that "made God sad." In a conversation around making mistakes a few years ago, we discussed how the devil thought he was perfect and that is how he fell from grace. My son turned to me and said, "So it seems the more we think we should be perfect, the more imperfect we are." He was five at the time, yet his words were so simple, wise, and true. The psalmist writes, "Out of the mouth of babes and nursing infants / You have ordained strength, / Because of Your enemies, / That You may silence the enemy and the avenger" (Psalm 8:2). My children teach me the power of simplicity. I am reminded of Jesus' admonishment: "Assuredly, I say to you, unless you are converted and become as little children, you will by no means enter the kingdom of heaven" (Matt. 18:3).

DAY 30

Pride

Acknowledging Our Need
for One Another and for God

Pride is denial of God. . . . Be exalted only by such achieve-
ments as you had before your birth. But what you received
after your birth, as also birth itself, God gave you. Only those
virtues which you have obtained without the co-operation of
the mind belong to you, because your mind was given you
by God. Only such victories as you have won without the co-
operation of the body have been accomplished by your efforts,
because the body is not yours, but a work of God.

—SAINT JOHN CLIMACUS[28]

One of the first tricks of the enemy against us is the idea of
trusting in oneself: that is, if not renouncing, then at least not
feeling the need for the help of Grace. The enemy as it were

---

28   *Ladder*, pp. 138–140.

says: "Do not go to the light where they wish to give you some kind of new powers. You are good just the way you are!"

—SAINT THEOPHAN THE RECLUSE[29]

One passion reproaches another: where there is self-esteem, avarice gives way—and it happens the other way around. We know, though, that sometimes all the vices leave a person, and only one remains with him—pride.

—SAINT MACARIUS[30]

For the Soul

Once an angel of unsurpassed beauty forgot that his glory was given by God and imagined it was of his own making. He believed he was greater than God and tried to rise above Him. The result was disastrous. The angel separated from God, and pride was the cause of his fall (Ezek. 28:13–17).

Pride is considered the chief of the passions. It caused the greatest of angels to fall from the heights of heaven. We, too, can be enticed to think our gifts are of our own making. Even the magnificence of our child can cause us to swell with pride. Recognizing our child as glorious is blameless—a child is a miracle to behold—so long as we recognize the mastery in the hand of God the Creator and direct our thanksgiving and honor to Him.

Here is another place where looking to the saints' examples can guide us. It is almost unfathomable for many of us how humble and God-fearing the saints were. This contrast is even more stark when we look around at our modern society, where the focus is

---

29   St. Theophan the Recluse, *The Path to Salvation: A Manual of Spiritual Transformation,* trans. Seraphim Rose (Platina, CA: St. Herman Press, 1997), pp. 33–35.

30   Rozhneva, "Pride, Vanity, and Self-Esteem."

often egocentric—all about what *I* need and want and how things can best serve *me*. Yet we have already described how during these early days of mothering our lives seem to be about anything but serving ourselves. In fact, we can feel quite the opposite: we exist in complete service to another with little to no time for thinking about our own needs, let alone desires.

We hope that in reading this book, in whatever way you have managed to do so over these past weeks, you have used some of the exercises to care for yourself and turn your thoughts, worries, joys, and struggles over to our Lord, the Theotokos, and the saints. While God already knows our thoughts and needs, in Matthew 7:7 we are reminded that we must still do the work of recognizing our needs and acknowledging God as our source of strength: "Ask, and it will be given you; seek, and you will find; knock, and it will be opened to you." We don't need to tell God anything; we just need to turn toward Him in prayer.

We may be in one of those moments of need now. We may need to hear that every mother has a hard time and needs help at one time or another. Each of us can get to a point where we need a break. Our arms are tired from nonstop baby-holding, or we can't get up and go to a crying baby one more time this night. When we get to this point and we think we just can't do it—all we want to do is cry, hide, run out the door and sit alone in the sunshine—we can practice humility (pride's greatest enemy) and recognize that we need help. We need someone else to hold the baby for a while. We need a long hot shower all to ourselves. We need a break.

～

Women need rest but also need connection and support. I would have loved a postpartum doula to come by and

encourage me. It would have been great to have a woman
from the church offer this kind of ministry.

—EMILY, ORTHODOX MOTHER

~

Pride can prevent us from recognizing we need help and asking for it, because we think we should be strong and able to do everything on our own, or we are embarrassed to need the care of others.

We likely have heard the phrase "It takes a village to raise a child." Traditionally, children were raised in community. Think of our biblical foremothers, such as Naomi, Ruth, Sarah, and Rachel, who raised families with sisters, mothers, and maid servants. Nowadays, many of us are isolated in raising our babies. But babies' needs haven't changed, and neither have ours. We have needs, and it is important to move past our own pride and allow ourselves to ask for and accept help.

Many women home with a new baby will assume that others are too busy, or they are afraid to be a bother. In truth, it's the opposite: most people don't want to bother a new mother! Especially women who have had children recognize how much help from others can mean. Any assistance—someone bringing a meal or groceries, taking the baby for an hour so we can rest or bathe, doing some tidying, or simply coming to visit and provide some adult company—can be an incredible blessing both for the receiver and the giver. Giving of our time and energy when we have some excess is a beautiful practice, and accepting help allows others the chance to give of themselves. Knowing that each of us has seasons where we have less and need more is essential in combating our own pride.

～

The forty days was difficult with my first because I felt over-whelmed and quite lonely. I wish I would have reached out for help, because now I realize how willing people are to help. I didn't want to bother anyone, but people want to help a new mother . . . myself included. Don't feel bad asking for company or help.

—ORTHODOX MOTHER

～

For Mind & Body

LETTING GO OF PERFECTION

When we are home with our brand-new babies, we spend an enormous amount of time trying to attend to their every need. When they struggle, we struggle. Sometimes even after we have fed, changed, kissed, and cuddled them, they are still crying, and all we can do is hold our baby in camaraderie, both of us miserable but at least together. These are some of the stressful and sacrificial moments of life with a newborn.

In these first days, an important part of babies' development is to show them that they are safe, they will be cared for and loved, and we and the world can meet their needs. This allows for healthy development and attachment.

During this time we may feel as if we have to do everything right, and if we don't know how to help our baby right away, we are not good mothers. We may have the illusion that if we were doing it all right, our baby would not cry. The truth is, even if we could be "perfect" mothers, our babies would still cry. Babies cry to communicate, to relieve tension, and sometimes just because. These moments can be very stressful. As mothers, we may blame ourselves, feeling we should know what is wrong and how to help right away. This is not true. Even when we are more experienced, we don't always know. Instead of fighting to be perfect, we can acknowledge how hard we are trying and allow ourselves to be humble in our role.

As our babies grow, and we grow in confidence and understanding of our individual child, we learn that we do not need to make every moment perfect. Twentieth-century British pediatrician and psychoanalyst D. W. Winnicott saw this as an important aspect of growth for both mother and child. He coined the term "Good Enough Mother"[31] to describe the healthy development of a mother and growing baby. A mother gradually allows for small disappointments and failures, which teach a child how to handle frustration and difficulty in a safe and loving space, so that he will eventually be able to handle the struggles of the world with resilience. Sometimes our baby may have to wait a few minutes for milk. As she is learning to do new things, she will get frustrated and struggle, and we won't help right away. These moments of growing independence will increase and lengthen over time until we are kissing our children goodbye and watching them drive themselves away from our homes. This is the normal and natural progression of growth and development. Our role is to allow our children to experience this in the safety of our love.

In letting go of the temptation to strive for perfection in mothering, we must acknowledge that this child was entrusted to us by God. We can view this as a big vote of confidence, knowing that He has faith in us to be our child's mother. We are enough, and as our child grows, we grow too. In our pride we may feel that it is all up to us. However, we must remember: *We are in God's hands*. We can be at peace knowing that ultimately it is

---

31   D. W. Winnicott, *Playing and Reality* (Routledge: London, 1971), p. 13.

God who guides and cares for our children. Our main job is to bring them to Him.

⁓

With my first baby, I worried about how I would ever learn to be a mother. Then I realized I had my child's whole lifetime to learn. For the moment, I only needed to be a mother of a baby; I could learn to be a mother of a toddler, a preschooler, a schoolgirl, a teenager as my child reached those stages. It was tremendously liberating!

—KATHERINE, ORTHODOX MOTHER

⁓

PART VII

The Higher Maternal Virtues

What I could not comprehend, however, until I was actually immersed in baby onesies and diapers, and getting but five interrupted hours of sleep a night, was how vast, demanding, fierce, and overwhelming maternal love could be. So vast, in fact, it couldn't fit in my pre-mom heart without repeatedly exploding it into a thousand tiny pieces and reconstructing it all over again, only bigger and more pliable each time.

—MOLLY SABOURIN[1]

---

1 Sabourin, "Motherhood."

Simplicity

Coming to God As We Are

Let all of us who wish to attract the Lord to ourselves draw near to Him as disciples to the Master, simply, without hypocrisy, without duplicity or guile, not out of idle curiosity. He Himself is simple and not composite, and He wants souls that come to Him to be simple and guileless.

—SAINT JOHN CLIMACUS[2]

Lord, my heart is not haughty,
Nor my eyes lofty.
Neither do I concern myself with great matters,
Nor with things too profound for me.
Surely I have calmed and quieted my soul,
Like a weaned child with his mother;
Like a weaned child is my soul within me.

—PSALM 131:1–2

---

2   *Ladder,* p. 148.

Seek the simplest in all things, in food, clothing, without being ashamed of poverty. For a great part of the world lives in poverty. Do not say, "I am the son of a rich man. It is shameful for me to be in poverty." Christ, your Heavenly Father, Who gave birth to you in the baptistery, is not in worldly riches. Rather he walked in poverty and had nowhere to lay His head.

—SAINT GENNADIUS OF CONSTANTINOPLE[3]

For the Soul

Saint John makes it quite clear how we are to come to the Lord. We are to approach Him simply, with no pretext, no explanations or excuses for where we've been. What a blessing that in each moment we can simply come to God as we are: tired, covered in spit-up, unwashed, as so many of us find ourselves in these early days of motherhood. We approach with simply our heart, our offering of ourselves, and a desire to learn from Him what we should do. *We start where we are.*

As St. Simeon does, we too should ask the Lord, "Grant me to say boldly that which I desire, O my Christ. Or rather, teach me what I ought to do and say."[4] This is a call for simplicity in our lives so that we can create space to hear the voice of God. For some of us, coming to God may be the first hard step. For others, approaching God may be easy, but knowing what to do when we are near, how to discern His voice from everything else in our lives, may be difficult.

We shared in DAY 24: NON-POSSESSIVENESS how we can

---

3   *The Golden Chain*, pp. 24–25. Orthodox Church Quotes, accessed May 9, 2021, https://www.orthodoxchurchquotes.com/2013/07/13/st-gennadi-us-of-constantinople-seek-the-simplest-in-all-things/.

4   Holy Trinity Monastery, "The Order of Preparatory Prayers for Holy Communion," *Prayer Book* (Jordanville, NY: Holy Trinity Monastery), p. 363.

physically clear space in our homes by being intentional with what we bring into our space. While this will simplify our external world, we also need to simplify our internal space. With a baby in arms, life becomes at once much more complex, and yet in some ways everything is much simpler. We are no longer able to move through the day as before. We find we need to build in an extra half hour, at least, before we go anywhere so we have time to prepare baby and handle any last-minute feeding or changes that come up. We must also reassess our priorities. Sometimes our babies just want to be held, or we need to rest, and the laundry, thank-you cards, and personal projects have to wait. We must let some things go. This also includes letting go of thoughts, worries, and to-dos that occupy our minds and take up precious energy, preventing us from being present in the moment. Christian writer Emily Freeman uses the term "soul minimalism"[5] to describe her process of letting go of the things that cloud her internal space. Whenever she feels clouded by daily cares, anxieties, or fear, she makes sure to set aside time to simplify her soul.

One of the main ways to start decluttering our souls is to invite silence into our day. We believe simplicity and "soul minimalism" come about through our prayers and in confession. In our prayers we can turn things over to God. We can give Him the worry about how our baby will get along if we go back to work or about paying the heating bill, our stress from the many demands on our time or an awkward conversation with a friend. All of these issues are legitimate concerns, and there may be concrete steps we can take to solve them, but we don't need to carry them with us all the time. We need to have a way to put them aside when we are not actively working on solving the problem. Praying to God to take the concern so we can free up space inside us can be a great gift.

---

5   *The Next Right Thing*, p. 26.

For Mind & Body

MORNING ROUTINE

The start of the day can set the tone for the simplicity or complexity of the day ahead. Depending on how our nights go (and for most of us this still means waking many times), we may opt for a few more minutes of precious sleep rather than rising before others in our household. In these early days, and until our baby sleeps some lengthy stretches, a little more sleep may very well be the best way to help ourselves cope with the many challenges and needs of the day. As we get more sleep and as we feel able, getting up ten minutes or more before baby (or asking our partner to take some morning time with baby) can be a good habit to develop as we move forward in motherhood. Having a clear start to the day can allow us to be clear in mind and purpose for the day ahead. Here are some ideas to get started.

➤ MORNING ROUTINE ◄

Suggestions for a Good Start

» While still in bed, say a short prayer or informally thank the Lord for the new day and for all the blessings in your life. Ask for strength to face whatever will come your way in the day ahead. We love the prayer of the Optina Elders ("God, grant me to greet the coming day in peace . . .").

» Stretch and drink a large glass of water.

» Even if you don't have time for formal prayers, stand in silence in your prayer corner or before an icon. Perhaps light a candle or vigil lamp and simply say a quiet prayer. This can be a nice time to have a piece of holy bread and a sip of holy water.

» Make a list of the three things most on your mind (maybe taken from your journal the night before) and one action you want to take today. Perhaps it is simply taking a walk or a nap.

» Have something nourishing to eat.

» Start your day!

~

Awake in the morning and the first thing you do, thank God for it, even if you don't feel particularly happy about the day which is to come. "This day which the Lord has made, let us rejoice and be grateful in it." Once you have done this, give yourself time to realise the truth of what you are saying and really mean it—perhaps on the level of deep conviction and not of what one might call exhilaration. And then get up, wash, clean; do whatever else you have to do, and then come to God again. Come to God with two convictions. The one is that you are God's own and the other is that this day is also God's own, it is absolutely new, absolutely fresh.

—METROPOLITAN ANTHONY OF SOUROZH[6]

~

---

6   *Beginning to Pray*, p. 75.

DAY 32

Humility

Use the Struggle to Grow in Faith and Love

Humility is a nameless grace in the soul, its name known only to those who have learned it by experience. It is unspeakable wealth, a name and gift from God, for it is said: Learn not from an angel, nor from man, nor from a book, but from Me, that is, from My indwelling, from my illumination and action in you; for I am meek and humble in heart and in thought and spirit, and your souls shall find rest from conflicts and relief from thoughts.

—SAINT JOHN CLIMACUS[7]

Blessed are the poor in spirit,
For theirs is the kingdom of heaven.

—MATTHEW 5:3

---

7   *Ladder*, p. 150.

But look; if we are humble, God helps us to fight our sinful-
ness; if we are proud, He does not. And how can we acquire
humility unless we are constantly humbled through seeing
ourselves as we are—the worst of sinners: Unless we are con-
stantly brought to our knees in penitence?

—ELDER MACARIUS OF OPTINA[8]

For the Soul

We've been journeying together, discovering the wonders and struggles of motherhood, for just over a month. Congratulations! What a long way we've come in this small amount of time. In the last week of our forty days together, we come to a crucial virtue for our spiritual well-being: humility. The more we understand humility, the more we see that it is a virtue that infuses all others and must be present at every moment of our spiritual journey. It is impossible to start along the ladder without it, and it is also a gift we receive as we grow in virtue.

We see in the quotes above and repeatedly throughout the Scriptures that God does not abide in those who lack humility, but with humility comes an abundance of spiritual gifts and aid: "For whoever exalts himself will be humbled, and he who humbles himself will be exalted" (Luke 14:11). "God resists the proud, / But gives grace to the humble" (James 4:6).

To attain the grace we seek, we must pursue humility as a hungry person would pursue food—as essential to our life and well-being. Yet do we even know what true humility is or where we begin in developing it? In all our, the authors', reading on the subject, which has been by no means exhaustive, we found three main themes and ways of approaching humility to be particularly

---

8   *Conquering Depression*, p. 45.

helpful: (1) putting others' needs and desires before our own; (2) focusing on our own faults and not those of others; and (3) pursuing gratitude toward God in all things.

~

As with the appearance of light, darkness retreats; so at the fragrance of humility, all anger and bitterness vanishes.

—SAINT JOHN CLIMACUS[9]

~

Motherhood can be a true gift in helping us cultivate humility in all three of these ways. To begin with, having children does much to help us subdue our ego. We are repeatedly asked to put our child(ren)'s needs before our own, continually given the chance to practice tempering our own needs and desires in order to attend to those of another. Sometimes we may even feel ourselves to be the servants of our children. And yet this is what we are called to be in all of life. Each year on the fifth Sunday of Great Lent we read the words of Christ: "Whoever desires to become great among you shall be your servant. And whoever of you desires to be first shall be slave of all. For even the Son of Man did not come to be served, but to serve, and to give His life a ransom for many" (Mark 10:43-45). We are all called to serve. While we may or may not have been blessed to have a profession that allowed us to be of service before motherhood, we are all now, as mothers, in a position to be constantly in service and to do the work of putting others before ourselves.

The second guide for beginning our pursuit of true and blessed humility is to turn our gaze inward at our own sinful nature and cast a blind eye to the sins and faults of others. The publican stood

---

9   *Ladder*, p. 81.

at the back of the temple and would not even lift his gaze upward, but bowed down to the floor and spoke simply and plainly, "God be merciful to me a sinner" (Luke 18:10–14). Just so we must turn our judging mind in upon ourselves each time it begins to find fault with others.

As we discussed in DAY 15: SLANDER, once we become mothers we can develop strong opinions on how mothering "should" be done. It is fine to apply these criteria to our own mothering (though we should always do so with kindness and compassion for our own mistakes), but we must be careful to hold back from applying our standards to others. We may notice ourselves passing judgment on our own parents, on the way our partners are relating to us and our babies, even on well-intentioned visitors or strangers offering a brief snippet of advice or encouragement. As mothers we are fiercely protective, but we must be careful that in our efforts to protect we don't become entangled in judgmental thoughts or criticisms that will sour our own souls.

Finally, motherhood, in and of itself, is a tremendous blessing and one for which we can work to be constantly grateful. We may not realize how difficult it can be for some people to have children, or we may have quickly forgotten how much we longed for them ourselves. Being grateful doesn't mean we will necessarily love being a mother at every moment. But we acknowledge having received a blessing that will, God willing, allow us for the rest of our lives many occasions for thanksgiving and awe.

In her book *The Scent of Holiness*, Matushka Constantina Palmer relates hearing the Cypriot priest-monk Archimandrite Zacharia of Essex state in a homily that there are two ways to acquire humility: "either by condemning yourself or by acquiring complete gratitude toward God."[10] Especially during this vul-

---

10   Constantina Palmer, *The Scent of Holiness* (Chesterton, IN: Ancient Faith

nerable postpartum time, seeing ourselves as the worst of sinners may not bring us to a sense of "nameless grace" at all, but rather to a place of despondency and despair. Instead, we can aim to "acquire gratitude in all things"—in the first coos of our baby, the ten tiny toes, *and* the seventeenth spit-up and second night in a row with no sleep. We can aim to "rejoice always," knowing that all of this is God's will, and choose to *use the struggle to grow in faith and love.*

SAINT JULIANA LAZAREVSKAYA (JANUARY 2/15)[11]

Russia, Sixteenth Century

Perhaps of all the saints who were mothers, St. Juliana's life may seem most like our own. She was not tested in martyrdom, nor did she become a monastic. She lived out her faith in day-to-day piety and humility, finding God in the routines of caring for home and children.

Throughout her life St. Juliana took great care of those in need. When she knew she was close to reposing, she called her children and those in the village to come to her bedside to share with them the importance of love, prayer, almsgiving, and good works. Right before she gave her soul to God, she said, "Glory to God for all. Into Thy hands I commend my spirit. Amen." At that moment a golden crown was seen around her head and fragrance filled the air.

Saint Juliana is a beautiful example to us of a mother living in the world whose love of God and care for those around her were a true example of Christian humility.

Publishing, 2012), p. 81.

11 *Marriage as a Path to Holiness*, pp. 96–101.

For Mind & Body

USING THE STRUGGLE

We are taught over and over by the wisdom of the Church Fathers and Mothers that struggle is given to us for our salvation. As implied by our golden rule, *use the struggle to grow in faith and love*, the struggle is not only something we can use but something we are given for our use. Whereas our pride tempts us to imagine that the difficulties that befall us are unfair and leads us to take offense at those who do something we don't like, we know that God allows us difficulties for our purification.

Through the beloved prayer of the Optina elders we pray, "Whatsoever news may reach me in the course of the day, teach me to accept it with a calm soul and the firm conviction that all is subject to Thy Holy will." And St. Ambrose of Optina reminds us as well:

> *A continuously happy life produces extremely unhappy consequences. In nature we see that there are not always pleasant springs and fruitful summers, and sometimes autumn is rainy and winter cold and snowy, and there is flooding and wind and storms, and moreover the crops fail and there are famine, troubles, sicknesses and many other misfortunes. All of this is beneficial so that man might learn through prudence, patience and humility. For the most part, in times of plenty he forgets himself, but in times of various sorrows he becomes more attentive to his salvation.*[12]

When we approach difficulties with the idea that they are placed in our lives as teachers of the virtues, we may find ourselves more

---

12   *Living without Hypocrisy*, p. 166.

able to receive them with a calm soul and redirect our disappointment or hurt into reflection and prayer.

➤ PRACTICE ◄
Finding Our Teachers

We chose to call this a practice because, for most of us, it requires an intentional change in the way we view and interact with difficulties as they arise in our lives. This practice aims to shift our perspective and invites us to rethink the role of disappointments and frustrations in our lives. It invites us to view difficulties as teachers sent from God to help us fight against our passions and perfect the virtues.

So often we are barely aware of the fact that we are reacting internally to something that has upset us. Perhaps it was an offhand comment by a friend or our partner. Perhaps we spilled the milk we prepared all over the counter *again*. Perhaps our baby is awake and crying just moments after we worked so hard to soothe him back down. We encounter so many small (and even large) frustrations each day that we often don't pause to notice how they are affecting us.

The first step in this practice is perhaps the hardest: recognizing when we are reacting negatively—with anger, impatience, wounded pride, or despondency. Often this recognition will happen after the incident, when we have more time and emotional distance to process. However, many of the rungs along St. John's ladder aim to help us create space and awareness of these passions as they flare up in the moment.

Once we become aware of our negative reaction, the next step is to employ our practice from DAY 10: MEEKNESS of pausing and taking a breath before we continue. Use this moment of pause to listen to your internal dialogue. In your frustration, anger, and impatience, are you blaming others? Yourself? Can you see the passion that is being ignited in you? Do you think your friend made that comment because she is jealous of you? Or because she is cruel? Did you spill the milk because you are clumsy? Or because you are so tired and no one lets you sleep? Is it your fault that your child woke up?

Next, assess what you could have done differently. If you responded in anger to your friend or gave her a harsh comment back, or if you berated yourself over the spilled milk or waking child, think about what you might have done if you had acted out of virtue instead of passion. Can you replace your negative, blaming thoughts with positive ones? Was your friend trying gently to let you know something? Can you give yourself grace in this moment?

The final step is to reflect and recognize the potential lesson in this experience. This may or may not lead to any immediate action, but in time we learn to recognize our passions as they arise and to quell them with the knowledge that we are being given a chance to learn and grow. Keeping the perspective that all things can be used toward our salvation, we can try to figure out what the teaching is in our trials. What virtue(s) are they helping us practice? What would help us better weather the storm of whatever passion we are being swept up in?

Our friend's or partner's comment may be a chance to recognize any truth in their words and to acknowledge our need for God's mercy. Or perhaps we find the insult completely untrue, but we are being given chance to turn the other cheek and practice meekness. The spilt milk, if we let it, can help us work on patience, humility, and forgiveness of ourselves. Attending yet again to our child can help us practice obedience and love. If we can try to remain curious about the lessons we are being offered and the teachers who are being placed in our path, we may be slower to react in pride and quicker to respond in humility.

~

A mother asks God to grant her patience. Let's say she's got the table set for dinner and the little child pulls the tablecloth, spilling everything on the floor. This is as if the child is saying to the mother, "Mom, be patient!"

—SAINT PAISIOS[13]

~

---

13 *Spiritual Counsels IV*, p. 164.

DAY 33

Discernment

Understanding God's Will

*Discernment in beginners is true knowledge of themselves;
in intermediate souls, it is a spiritual sense that faultlessly
distinguishes what is truly good from what is of nature and
opposed to it; and in the perfect, it is the knowledge which
they have within by Divine illumination, and which can
enlighten with its lamp what is dark in others. Or perhaps,
generally speaking, discernment is, and is recognized as, the
certain understanding of the Divine will on all occasions, in
every place and in all matters; and it is only found in those
who are pure in heart, and in body and in mouth.*

—SAINT JOHN CLIMACUS[14]

*It is discernment which in Scripture is described as the eye
and the lamp of the body. This is what the Saviour says, 'your
eye is the light of your body, and if your eye is sound then*

---

14   *Ladder*, p. 161.

there is light in your whole body. But if your eye is diseased then your entire body will be in darkness' (Matthew 6:22–23). This eye sees through all the thoughts and actions of a man, examining and illuminating everything which we must do. And if it is not sound in a man, that is, if it is not fortified by good judgment and by well-founded knowledge, if it is deluded by error and by presumption, this makes for darkness in our entire body.

—SAINT JOHN CASSIAN[15]

True wisdom is gazing at God. Gazing at God is silence of the thoughts. Stillness of mind is tranquility which comes from discernment.

—SAINT ISAAC THE SYRIAN[16]

For the Soul

Saint John's definition of discernment is knowing the will of God at all times. What an incredible gift! How often do we wish we knew what God wanted us to do? How much more true is this now that we are mothers and responsible not only for ourselves but for at least one other precious soul? Even before we had children, we made so many decisions on a day-to-day basis. Now, as mothers, we've added a thousand small decisions to our list: When should we put baby down for a nap? Is it okay if she cries a little? There will be other questions to come, and bigger ones. What kind of an education will we provide for our children? How do we teach our children to pray and to love God? How do we continue to learn to pray and love God ourselves?

---

15 John Cassian, *Conferences*, trans. Colm Luibheid. Classics of Western Spirituality (Mahwah, NJ: Paulist Press, 1985), pp. 61–63.
16 *A Monk's Topical Bible A–D*, p. 308.

Historically, people—especially women—didn't have as many choices. There was simply less flexibility, fewer options, and more societal norms. Nowadays the possibilities seem infinite. The options are boggling, and we spend a lot more time than we realize just deciding what brand of milk to buy or which car seat is safest.

In 2006, a group of psychologists coined the term "decision fatigue"[17] to describe the unrest and exhaustion that can come from having to make so many daily decisions. In this state of fatigue people tend to make poor decisions. Much research has gone into how we can best avoid this burnout. Not surprisingly, a major way to combat decision fatigue is to have a personal philosophy on which to base our decisions. We would posit here that one such philosophy—founded in our Orthodox Faith—is to choose to love and pray always.

⁓

Do not be conformed to this world, but be transformed by the renewal of your mind, that by testing you may discern what is the will of God, what is good and acceptable and perfect.
—ROMANS 12:2 (ESV)

⁓

Within our Faith we are blessed to have guidance for many areas of our life. We have restrictions on what foods we eat at certain times. We reserve our Sundays for worship and community. Perhaps we dress more conservatively than most. We have lots of

---

17   Kathleen D. Vohs, Roy F. Baumeister, Jean M. Twenge, "Decision Fatigue Exhausts Self-Regulatory Resources," *Psychology Today*, accessed July 8, 2020, https://www.psychologytoday.com/files/attachments/584/decision200602-15vohs.pdf.

guidance on how and when to pray and how much we should give to the poor and how much in support of our church communities. While some may see this guidance as restrictive, many of us have felt the ease of having some of our decisions made easier by it.

Indeed, we may wish that God's will were more apparent to us in the many choices we must make when our Faith gives us no clear answer. In His infinite wisdom and mercy, God gave us an example of perfection in human form in His Son, Jesus Christ. While we don't know each detail of how Jesus lived while here on earth, we do know that He always acted out of love—even unto the Cross. He commanded us to do the same: "A new commandment I give to you, that you love one another; as I have loved you, that you also love one another. By this all will know that you are My disciples, if you have love for one another" (John 13:34–35). From this we learn that we can follow God's will by simply trying to act from a place of love.

Orthodox writer Nancy Holloway writes about this connection between discernment and love: "Discernment is seen by the Church Fathers as one of the greatest and more difficult of the virtues. Yet discernment is needed if we are to know in each circumstance of our life, how to love, how to express it, how to move from self to selflessness." She ends the thought with the key to discernment: "Critical to discernment is a rich and deep life of prayer."[18] Again we are brought full circle—*prayer is the way.*

While the perfect discernment we strive for may be knowing God's will, we must start with an understanding of our own will. Saint John writes that "a true knowledge of ourselves is discernment in beginners." This starts with being honest about who we are, our priorities, and our motives. Our conscience will be a helpful guide along this path as we pray for insight from God. In

---

18   *The Maternity of Mary*, p. 85.

Living Prayer, Met. Anthony Bloom says we must ask the Lord, "Help me, O God, to put off all pretences and find my true self."[19] For this we must pray.

As we mention throughout the book, prayer right now will be different. We may rarely, if ever, have the extended times for prayer we had before we had children, and yet we are still called to pray always. With the new responsibilities and decisions to be made, we must arguably pray even more. Thankfully, we can begin to recognize more and more that each moment is an opportunity for prayer. This allows us to deepen our prayer life, not only calling on the Lord formally but keeping His praise continually in our mouths (Psalm 34:1). This true and deep life of prayer, as Holloway says, will allow us to develop our own internal sense of knowing—knowledge given by "divine illumination"[20] inside us.

In taking moments to pray to God and listening in the quiet spaces of our lives for His answers, we can begin to develop discernment. Saint John gives us advice on how to continue: "In all your undertakings and in every way of life . . . let it be your rule and practice to ask yourself: Am I really doing this in accordance with God's will?"[21] We may not always know the answer, but, in asking the question, we can humble ourselves and recognize our need for guidance.

This guidance can be found by following our Lord and God and Savior Jesus Christ's example and always choosing to act from a place of love. If we are guided by love and remain connected to God through frequent prayer, we can focus on the next

---

19   Anthony Bloom, *Living Prayer* (Springfield, IL: Templegate Publishers, 1974).

20   *Maternity of Mary*, p. 161.

21   *Ladder*, p. 175.

decision and then the one that follows, trusting that God will be guiding us and providing for our families.

SARAH

In the past I haven't known how to label my parenting style. In writing this chapter, I've realized that my goal is to parent with discernment. I use my Christian faith and an understanding of who I want my children to grow to be to guide my day-to-day choices. As mothers we have so many choices to make for ourselves and our children. We must decide what foods to eat, how to dress, how we spend time, when we go to church, etc. Such questions bombard us, and very soon the voices of our children will chime in with their own desires, which are often contrary to ours.

As my children grow, I see that not only must I use discernment in my choices, but I am teaching them how to be discerning as well. In our family we don't go to birthday parties on Sunday mornings. Our kids have learned that Sunday morning is reserved for worship, and many of their friends who would like to have our kids at their parties have learned this too. As my eldest daughter is now an independent reader, we have to use discernment in her reading choices. Together we discuss books and why they may be good choices for her or not. We try to read wisely, because stories live in our hearts and minds and shape us.

These are the daily choices I must make as a parent, and through my decisions I am teaching my children how to make their own choices. How do I know the right path? I pray that I am able to seek the guidance of the Lord and do my best to use discernment born from prayer and obedience to God's commandments.

For Mind & Body

HOW WE MAKE CHOICES

While doing our best to pray, love, and follow God's will, we can also use some concrete and practical steps in making decisions. We speak about finding and following God's will and using discernment, yet we may wonder how this applies to the daily tasks of baby care and household management. Whenever a decision needs to be made, it is helpful to have a general approach to help us tune into God's guiding presence even in our seemingly trivial day-to-day choices.

➤ PRACTICE ◀

A System for Decision Making

Setting Priorities and Routines

While we as Christians have many guiding principles based on trying to live in a Christlike way, we may not consult them explicitly in making our day-to-day decisions. Remembering that we are trying to live according to God's will and word and to "seek first the kingdom of God" (Matt. 6:33) can help guide our decision making.

To identify our priorities, we can use any of a number of systems. We were introduced to using the five Ps, a way of ordering what is important in a mother's life, set out by Holly Pierlot in *A Mother's Rule of Life*. Pierlot's five Ps are *prayer* (our worship and devotion to God), *person* (caring for ourselves so we can care for others), *partner* (our love, care, and availability for our partner), *parent* (our love, care, and availability for our child/ren), *provider* (our work in the home, outside of the home, and in our church and community).[22] Holly advises making sure we are caring for and devoting time to each of these areas of our life, in that order.

Many decisions we make revolve around how we spend our time as we try to find time for the things we need and want to do. Setting our priorities and making routines can help us in this process. This can be done in many ways. Our day-to-day activities can be organized around what is most important to us. We can simplify the daily decisions we need to make by making a bunch of them all at once: creating a daily meal plan, a weekly schedule, and a rotating list of chores. In the classic series *Little House on the Prairie*, Ma had her system: "Wash on Monday, Iron on Tuesday, Mend on Wednesday, Churn on Thursday, Clean on Friday, Bake on Saturday, and Rest on Sunday."[23] While our modern routine may be a little different, establishing order in the way we do what is needed can bring peace. We set aside time weekly, monthly, or yearly, when we can put our full attention to the task, to review and revise our systems and priorities. For example, getting to the end of the day knowing what is for dinner can make a tremendous difference not only in the quality of our evening but also in the quality of our diet.

Limiting Options

Our tasks and choices can often seem unlimited. There are myriad ways to spend and give our time, endless chores to

---

22   Holly Pierlot, *A Mother's Rule of Life: How to bring order to your home and peace to your soul* (Nashua, NH: Sophia Institute Press, 2004), p. 18.

23   Laura Ingalls Wilder, *Winter Days in the Big House* (Scholastic: New York, 1995).

be done. Even within a limited budget we still have many choices of what to buy, and we can often feel we are spinning our wheels. We can protect ourselves from letting the sheer number of choices available drain our God-given time and energy by limiting our options. Using our priorities as a guide, we can allot time for chores, work, leisure, and worship and narrow down within each of these categories what choices we have. In managing our food shopping and household needs, we can choose a single favorite place for the bulk of our food shopping, a reliable review site, or a trusted friend to make choices simpler. If possible, finding thrift stores for purchasing clothes and items for children can significantly limit our options while playing a role in environmental stewardship.

Asking Important Questions and Reflecting on Motives

In making decisions, we can also spend time praying and examining our motives. Is our desire to throw a big birthday party born out of vanity and a wish for others to recognize us, or out of some other passion? We can ask ourselves, is this a need or a want? We may want to have a perfectly clean house or try a new recipe or catch up on social media, but is this a need? Can simple tidying and clean clothes suffice so we can spend time baby gazing or have a few extra minutes to take a walk and get some fresh air? The questions are important to ask, allowing us to reflect and bring them to God, but the answers aren't always so clear.

To help us with this we can ask a simple question: "Is it life-giving or life-draining?" In *The Next Right Thing*, a book about making decisions rooted in listening to God's voice in our lives, author Emily Freeman asks this question in making decisions and in reflecting on past choices.[24] We will know which category something falls into by how we feel when we sit with the question in prayerful silence and the energy we feel around our choices. Some things that are seemingly life-draining we can't avoid, such as diaper changing and cleaning toilets, but these ultimately are in the service of caring for our family, which can be life-giving. Other life-draining things, such as toxic relationships, may be best to take a break from, especially during this vulnerable time in our lives. Take time, perhaps over the next week, to notice when decisions need to be made and slow the process down internally. If we sit with our choices, we may find one or the other more fully leads us toward seeking the Kingdom of God.

---

24   *The Next Right Thing*, p. 99.

PART VIII

Finding God

His purpose for your motherhood is that you would know him better, love him more, depend completely on his strength, and understand faithfulness in a new way. God made you a mom to draw you deeper into his love and his story.

—MAGGIE COMBS[1]

1   Maggie Combs, "God's Unexpected Purpose for Motherhood," *Risen Motherhood* (blog), April 2, 2018, https://www.risenmotherhood.com/blog/gods-unexpected-purpose-for-motherhood.

DAY 34

Stillness

Being Present

Stillness of the body is the knowledge and composure of the habits and feelings. And stillness of the soul is the knowledge of one's thoughts and an inviolable mind. A friend of stillness is a courageous and decisive thought which keeps constant vigil at the doors of the heart, and kills or repels the thoughts that come. He who practices silence with perception of heart will understand this last remark.

—SAINT JOHN CLIMACUS[2]

When you retreat into yourself, you should stand before the Lord, and remain in his presence. . . . This is the true wilderness—to stand face to face with the Lord. The state of standing before the Lord is something that supports and maintains itself.

—SAINT THEOPHAN THE RECLUSE[3]

---

2   *Ladder*, p. 198.

3   St. Theophan the Recluse, quoted in *Art of Prayer: An Orthodox Anthology*,

So we no longer pursue plainness and simplicity of life. We no longer value stillness, which helps to free us from past defilement, but prefer a whole host of things which distract us uselessly from our true goal.

—SAINT NEILOS THE ASCETIC[4]

For the Soul

Stillness is foreign to most of our modern-day lives. It is certainly not a quality actively sought by secular culture, which seems to worship constant activity, noise, doings, and distractions. In our spiritual understanding, stillness allows us to come into the presence and awareness of God. "Be still, and know that I *am* God," the psalmist says (Psalm 46:10). In stillness, we quell our activity and make room to recognize His activity in us. Stillness precedes prayer on the ladder, as it is preparation for a prayerful heart. It is in stillness that we lay the foundation for connection with God.

In the early days with a baby, we may find we are more physically still than in the past. If this is our first child, we may find ourselves surrounded by stillness due to the complete shift of daily routines. If this is not our only child, quiet moments with our baby likely do exist—even if only in the middle of the night. While, as we discussed on DAY 4: EXILE, there may be a palpable absence of busyness as we used to know it, internal stillness may still feel far away. Our minds are full of new worries ("Is she still breathing?"), new hopes ("Look at that smile!"), new questions ("When should we plan our first trip?"), and new judgments ("I shouldn't have let him stay awake so long"). Our bodies may be quiet, but our minds are abuzz.

ed. Igumen Charion, trans. E. Kadloubovsky and E. M. Palmer (New York: Faber and Faber, 1997), p. 254.

4   "Ascetic Discourse," *The Philokalia*, vol. 1, p. 203.

Research shows that most people spend about 47 percent of their waking hours in a state that has been dubbed the "default mode."[5] The default mode is where our brain tends to go when we aren't actively thinking about anything else. It is an unfocused mental state where thoughts run wild—ruminating, worrying, planning, judging, and remembering. This time spent in default mode is exhausting and is responsible for about 80 percent of our brain's energy consumption each day.[6] Through years of doing things on automatic pilot and multitasking, we have created pathways in our brain that effectively hardwire us for distraction and a lack of awareness.

How many new behaviors have we been engaging in as if on autopilot in this last month while feeding, diapering, burping, and rocking? Have we noticed that we can spend an entire ten or fifteen minutes feeding our child without ever actually paying attention to what is happening? Without noticing the way our baby's tiny hands are opening and closing or hearing the gentle sucks and swallows? Where has our mind been? Often we find we have gone down a rabbit hole of negative thoughts, brewing worry and anxiety or replaying disagreements or conflicts. Even simply daydreaming, planning, or reminiscing distracts us.

This can be even more noticeable and damaging when we are trying to commune with God. While praying, St. John instructs, "let us be still and undistracted. For by distractions, the demons aim to bring our prayer to nothing."[7] Likely all of us have felt this at one time or another. When reading Scripture or prayers, how

---

5   Matthew A. Killingsworth and Daniel T. Gilbert, "A wandering mind is an unhappy mind," National Library of Medicine, Nov. 12, 2010, https://pubmed.ncbi.nlm.nih.gov/21071660/.

6   Marcus E. Raichle, et al., "A default mode of brain function," *PNAS* 98, no. 2 (January 16, 2001), pp. 676–682.

7   *Ladder*, p. 46.

often do we notice a whole paragraph or page has gone by without our having any idea of what we just read? In the beautiful and meditative services of our Church, how often do we find our minds planning dinner or rehashing a difficult moment from the past week?

It can be upsetting to awaken to how distracted we are in our daily lives. Beginning to notice how much our minds wander can be a hard but important first step in cultivating stillness. Creating stillness may look passive, but it is active and requires effort. Anyone who has observed small children trying to be still in church, at prayers, or in a line at the store can see that stillness does not come naturally to us in our fallen state. We must take time to commit ourselves, prepare ourselves, and create time and space for stillness in our lives. We can begin to cultivate stillness within by cultivating moments of stillness externally.

For most of us still in the early stages of our ascent of this divine ladder, outward stillness can be extremely helpful in this process. God made us of both body and soul, and thus the physical part of us affects the spiritual part, and vice versa. Cultivating external stillness can be a helpful entry point into developing and fostering internal stillness.

Physical stillness can be literal, in that we take quiet moments to be still: standing, sitting, contemplating without rushing around, holding our baby while he sleeps, or lying in the grass and watching the clouds. Giving ourselves quiet moments of physical stillness can calm us and prepare our minds for internal stillness. Physical stillness can also happen when we are doing something, such as changing a diaper or taking a walk, if we bring our thoughts and activity into a single focus. As we quiet our body into stillness, we start to quiet our minds and bring stillness into our hearts. We do this by focusing on the task at hand. We narrow our focus to what is before us, stilling the distractions and thoughts by bringing our attention to the present moment—its details, sounds, and sensations.

The present moment is where we encounter God. God is not in the past or in the future. He is here with us now, in each moment. When we are focused in the present, we can meet Him. In Luke 17:20–21 Jesus admonishes the Pharisees, saying, "The kingdom of God does not come with observation; nor will they say, 'See here!' or 'See there!' For indeed, the kingdom of God is within you." God is always with us; we are the ones who need to still the world inside to recognize this. To find Him we must connect with our internal stillness and dwell in the present moment. Being present is being aware of what is within and around us, which includes God. This awareness expands our sense of time, allowing us to slow down and be conscious of what we are doing, or in the case of finding stillness, not doing. This honing of our attention can bring stillness to the waters of our soul that can permeate our day regardless of the stillness or lack thereof around us.

When we are pulled from this attention and get caught up in distracting thoughts that take us from the present moment into the past or future, we can call the Jesus prayer into our hearts and minds. "Lord Jesus Christ, son of God, have mercy on me, a sinner." We see beautiful examples of stillness and presence in monks and nuns who constantly practice the Jesus prayer. There is no doubt that keeping the prayer of Jesus on our lips is one of the most accessible and efficacious ways of keeping our minds focused on Christ. We may find that distractions creep in, but bringing our focus back to our prayer and into stillness and awareness in the present moment will strengthen us and prepare us for meeting God.

These are the small steps we can take toward cultivating this important virtue. A crying baby can bring anxiety and tension to a mother, but even changing our crying baby's diaper can be as much a prayerful and still activity as sitting quietly, if we do it with attention, love, and prayer. Coming to our child with such stillness can also help soothe our child. *Our peace brings peace.* During this time, we can practice stillness in our heart and work to accept the change in rhythm as an opportunity to grow more and more present with God.

SASHA

In writing this I appreciate how much I have struggled against stillness most of my life. After my first child was born, I was completely thrown off by the stillness. I had just finished a busy medical residency and all of a sudden was home alone with a baby who didn't speak or interact much at all, except to cry. The stillness felt overwhelming. I threw myself into new activities—moms' groups, long walks in the woods or by the water carrying my sleeping son, watching mindless TV shows and social media.

When my daughter was born, my son was two, and I again left little time for stillness, enjoying instead having my older child around for company. It wasn't until my third child was born that it finally began to sink in how short those early days really are. Finally I began to allow time for more stillness. How distracted I have been! And yet I also see now how, slowly over the six years since my first child was born, I have allowed more and more stillness to come in. I have come to recognize how vital it is to me—both personally and as a parent—and how much lighter, more centered and connected with God I feel when I cultivate stillness in my life.

For Mind & Body

LIVING IN THE NOW

Practicing being in the moment can strengthen our ability to be present and find stillness. Below we offer some activities and ideas for helping us to be present every day.

Weave the Jesus prayer into daily tasks. Bring the Jesus prayer into routine daily activities with your baby. Consider saying the prayer aloud. Imagine the spiritual benefit for your child of having these words engraved, as it were, on her soul.

Spend time outside. No matter what the weather, make time to be outside. If the season is favorable, sit outside and feed your baby. Consider finding a patch of grass and taking off your shoes, enjoying the feel of grass on your feet. If it's cold, bundle up and find a space to be in nature. As you are out and about more and more in the coming weeks, seek out water, parks, and forests to be in the glory of God's creation with your child(ren).

Practice baby gazing. See activity in THANKSGIVING, page 134.

Move your body. One way to practice being present is to bring our attention to our body. Most of the time we are so focused on our thoughts that we pay little attention to our physical bodies. When we move and let ourselves listen, feel, and be in our bodies, we come into the here and now. We tune into our sensations, our feelings, the impulse to move our arm this way, to sway our head or move to a beat. Dancing is one way to practice while having fun, boosting endorphins, calming your baby, and getting some exercise. Put on some rhythmic and joyful music. You can hold your baby and gently dance and sway together; or if your baby is happy alone, feel free to dance for your baby. Notice how your body feels; focus on staying in the moment with your baby and yourself. If other children are around, feel free to invite them to join in for a family dance.

~

Whoever lives in the past is like a dead man. Whoever lives in the future in his imagination is naïve, because the future belongs to God. The Joy of Christ is found only in the Present, in the Eternal Present God.

—MOTHER GAVRILIA[8]

~

---

8   "Sayings of Mother Gavrilia," *Holy Trinity Family Blogspot* (blog), May 9, 2015, https://holytrinityfamily.blogspot.com/2015/05/sayings-of-mother-gavrilia-1992.html.

Prayer

Prayer Is the Way

Have all courage, and you will have God for your teacher in prayer. Just as it is impossible to learn to see by word of mouth, because seeing depends on one's own natural sight, so it is impossible to learn the beauty of prayer from the teaching of others. Prayer has a Teacher all its own—God—that teacheth man knowledge, and grants the prayer of him who prays, and blesses the years of the just. Amen.

—SAINT JOHN CLIMACUS[9]

It is sometimes well during prayer to say a few words of our own, breathing fervent faith and love to the Lord. . . . Moreover, we grow too accustomed to the words of others and grow cold in prayer. And how pleasing to the Lord this lisping of our own is, coming directly from a believing, loving, and thankful heart. It is impossible to explain this: it is only needful to say

---

9   *Ladder*, p. 220.

*that when you are praying to God with your own words the
soul trembles with joy, it becomes wholly inflamed, vivified,
and beatified. . . . When praying, keep to the rule that it is
better to say five words from the depth of your heart than ten
thousand words with your tongue only.*

—SAINT JOHN OF KRONSTADT[10]

*Pray to God with open arms. This is the secret of the saints.
As soon as they opened their arms, they were visited by divine
grace. As the most effective prayer the Church Fathers use
the short phrase, "Lord Jesus Christ, have mercy on me." This
prayer is the key to the spiritual life. It is a prayer that cannot
be taught either by books, or by spiritual fathers or by anyone
else. Its sole teacher is divine grace.*

—SAINT PORPHYRIOS[11]

For the Soul

Throughout this book we offer the words of saints, holy fathers
and holy mothers. They are the experts in the matters of the
soul because they devoted their lives, often in seclusion or great
torment, to finding the truth of God. What we learn from them
again and again is that to commune with God, we must find true
and deep prayer of the heart.

In the church we both grew up in, our priest, Fr. Spyridon,
always described prayer as lighting a candle within our hearts—
igniting the light of Christ that shines within us and from us
throughout our day. This image was powerful for us as children, and now that we are adults it resonates still. Saint John of

---

10   *My Life in Christ*, pp. 105–106.
11   *Wounded by Love*, p. 119.

Kronstadt writes that moments of sincere prayer work immediately to make our soul "vivified, warm, and fruitful." He continues, "The wilderness of the soul blossoms like a lily at the coming of the Lord into the heart. Oh, why do we not turn our hearts oftener towards the Lord? How much peace and comfort ever lie concealed in Him for us!"[12]

While the rhythm of our lives changes when we become mothers, the meaning of our life remains the same. Our need and desire for connection with God is perhaps even greater now than ever. We need not feel overwhelmed by the thought of integrating prayer here! Each and every moment is an opportunity for prayer—small prayers of thanksgiving, prayers while changing a diaper, prayers on lying down to rest. Prayer can be simply connecting with God by saying "Lord, have mercy on me." We can let our love be unceasing prayer within us.

⁓

My kids have been little flames of faith pulling me toward God. I pray more because I pray with and for them.

—CASEY, ORTHODOX MOTHER

⁓

Prayer is perhaps the easiest and, at the same time, most difficult thing we are called to do as Christians. Easiest because, in essence, prayer is simply speaking with God; and yet hardest because it is here, it seems, more than in any other area of our lives, that the devil works his most subtle and effective warfare. How often are we too tired, don't have time, feel insincere in reading our prayers, or simply get out of the habit? How can we forget to make time for that which is most needful? Here in this

---

12 *My Life in Christ*, pp. 103–104.

last week of our spiritual wanderings in the wilderness of new motherhood, we come to the greatest challenge—living in prayer.

Living in prayer is inviting God into our lives and hearts. It is keeping Him in our mind and praying throughout the day. As we discussed in DAY 34: STILLNESS, creating space in our hearts for God prepares us for meeting Him in prayer. It is in the stillness of our heart and mind that we can hear His call and become aware of His presence. These are our efforts to create a prayerful life. The beauty of it is that we aren't the ones who have to perfect it. We bring Him our efforts, but it is God's mercy and grace that transforms us. "Lift up your gates, O ye princes; and be ye lifted up, ye everlasting gates, and the King of Glory shall enter in."[13] We open ourselves to God, and He comes to dwell in us.

While so much of our spiritual life is internal, the fruits of our prayer and diligence are brought forth in action. Just as repentance is a change of heart (metanoia), the truth of our repentance shows when our actions match the intentions of our heart—when we apologize for hurting someone, when we help someone in need. The same is true of our prayer. Abbot Tryphon of Vashon writes of prayer, "The true and undying strength of our prayer lies in the depths of our soul which lead to good works and pious acts of virtue that reach every part and every action of our life."[14]

As we grow in our prayer life—in simply remembering God prayerfully throughout our day, calling to Him, thanking Him, pausing before a task to ask Him for strength—our actions will reflect this and will model and embody prayer for our children as well. It is a beautiful cycle. The more we pray, the more we know

---

13   Psalm 23, *The Prayer Book*, p. 333.
14   Abbot Tryphon, "Unceasing Prayer," *The Morning Offering* (blog), Ancient Faith Ministries, July 17, 2019, https://blogs.ancientfaith.com/morningof-fering/2019/07/unceasing-prayer/.

God; the more we know God, the more we desire to do good and seek Him out in prayer.

⌒

During my second round of postpartum life, I discovered the Akathist to the Mother of God, Nurturer of Children. I still pray it almost daily.

—CAITLIN, ORTHODOX MOTHER

⌒

SASHA

In looking back, I can see that when I first became a mother, prayer was palpably absent. My prayer book collected dust on the shelf, and I felt so caught up in the act of simply keeping this tiny human alive, clean, fed, and rested, as well as caring for myself in the same ways, that I don't remember praying at all. God forgive me! In truth I see that my prayer life from before motherhood was lacking and overly formalized. And if I thought I didn't have time then—in the midst of my medical training—I somehow had even less now.

With my second and third children, prayer began to feel more natural. It became a part of our family rhythm. I relaxed into the idea that, while formal prayer is still necessary and fundamental, informal prayer can and should, I believe, become the bulk of our prayer. Every moment is an opportunity for prayer and everything an occasion for prayer if I remember to let it be so. This new understanding and relationship with God has been life-changing and life-giving. Now all I have to do is pray for the grace to remember to pray more and more!

SAINT NONNA (AUGUST 5/18)

Cappadocia, Fourth Century

Saint Nonna was a model of Christian life and raised one of the holiest families in history, as both her husband and children were canonized as saints. One of her sons was St. Gregory the Theologian, the other St. Caesarius, and her daughter St. Gorgonia. We know much of how St. Nonna was viewed as a mother and wife from the words of her son. She was revered as a woman who had God foremost in her heart and taught her children, through her example, of the importance of prayer in a Christian life. Saint Gregory said of her, "What time or place for prayer has ever escaped her? Each day this has been more important for her than everything else."[15]

Let us remember prayer as a focus of our life and pray to St. Nonna for her intercessions in our own mothering and prayer life.

➤ PRACTICE ◄

How to Pray

Let your prayer be completely simple. For both the publican and the prodigal son were reconciled to God by a single phrase.

—SAINT JOHN CLIMACUS[16]

∿

Prayer is the hallmark of a heart reaching for God, and in our role as mothers, it is the salve for every wound. *Prayer*

---

15   *Marriage as a Path to Holiness*, p. 92.
16   *Ladder*, p. 213.

is the way. Saint John Climacus gives us a recipe for simple and sincere prayer of the heart. He writes, "Before all else, let us list sincere thanksgiving first on the scroll of our prayer. On the second line we should put confession and heartfelt contrition of soul. Then let us present our petition for the King of all."[17]

When we come to the Lord in prayer, let us try to hold this structure in our minds.

» Giving thanks

» Confession

» Petition

~

Pray pray pray. "Give me strength and guide me."
—PATTY, ORTHODOX MOTHER

~

For Mind & Body

GET OUTSIDE

Being in nature, away from manmade creation and in God's space, is very prayerful. In nature we are surrounded by a different kind of stillness and are often more able to stand in silent awe at the complexity and beauty of the world God created for us. We encourage you to try to get a few minutes outside each day so that you and your baby can connect with the natural world. Even if you are still recovering and not comfortable moving much, take time to sit outside with your baby. Take these forty days (or more)

---

17   Ibid, p. 213.

when you are home to notice how nature shifts and changes from day to day and from season to season. Take small walks around your neighborhood if you feel up for it, and plan where you will go for longer walks or hikes when you are recovered and your baby is ready to explore the world. Being in nature is restorative to us. It is the natural world God created for our joy and to provide for us. Take this gift of nourishment as often as you can.

~

O Lord, how good it is for us to be Thy guests! How fine it is for us in Thy world. The fields are fragrant, the mountains rise high up into the sky, and the golden rays of sun and the light clouds are reflected in the water. All nature mysteriously speaks about Thee, all is filled with Thy mercy and all carries the seal of Thy love. Blessed be the earth which, with her short-lasting beauty, awakens the yearning for the eternal homeland in Thy kingdom, where in everlasting beauty resounds the song: Alleluia!

—KONTAKION 2, "AKATHIST OF THANKSGIVING"

~

Dispassion

A Spirit of Peace

The soul has dispassion which is immersed in virtues as the passionate are in pleasures.

—SAINT JOHN CLIMACUS[18]

Finally, after long labors and exertions, the Christian principles appear victorious, reigning without opposition; they penetrate the whole composition of human nature, dislodging from the demands and inclinations hostile to themselves, and place it in a state of passionlessness and purity, making it worthy of the blessedness of the pure in heart—to see God in themselves in sincerest communion with Him.

—SAINT THEOPHAN THE RECLUSE[19]

I think that man is called a peacemaker par excellence who pacifies perfectly the discord between flesh and spirit in

---

18   *Ladder*, p. 222.
19   *Raising them Right*, p. 9.

himself and the war that is inherent in nature, so that the law of the body no longer wars against the law of the mind, but is subjected to the higher rule and becomes a servant of the Divine ordinance.

—SAINT GREGORY OF NYSSA[20]

For the Soul

As Christians, we are given to struggle. We struggle against the passions of our body and soul. We struggle against the current of the world, trying to avoid being caught up in desires for wealth, praise, or vanity. We struggle to subdue these passions, and in this we hope to reach the higher levels of spiritual life, where we find our passions do not sway us as much. Our virtues will then become the dominant forces in our lives, and we will be able to discern God's will. This is a movement toward dispassion, where we have escaped the vise grip of passions and are able to draw closer to God.

Dispassion is a state of being that is sought after by the most pious of monastics. It can seem like an unattainable goal for most of us, especially in this tender time when we are likely feeling emotions and temptations quite intensely. As with every aspect of our spiritual life, we are each in our own place, and while dispassion may not be where we are, we can gain a sense of its purpose and beauty and work to move toward it in our own lives in whatever way we can. *We start where we are.*

As mothers of newborns, we may be noticing that our inclination toward certain passions is different now than it was just a few months ago. If we tended toward anger before, we may instead

---

20 St. Gregory of Nyssa, "7th Beatitude: Blessed Are the Peacemakers," *Orthodox Way of Life* (blog), September 17, 2009, http://orthodoxwayoflife. blogspot.com/2009/09/7th-beatitude-blessed-are-peacemakers.html.

find ourselves slipping frequently into worry. If we suffered from strong vanities, we may now be swept up in despondency. We may also find that we respond to the passions differently. Perhaps we find that instead of causing us to cry, despondency makes us irritable; or instead of inciting anger, impatience makes us tearful. To move toward dispassion, we can begin by recognizing the passions as they arise in us. We can then turn to God, the Theotokos, and the saints in prayer to ask for help in easing them.

To perceive the passions early, before they begin to take root, we need to be aware of our own internal state. The beauty of St. John's ladder is that each step builds on the last and opens up further avenues for renewing our baptism and uncovering God's presence in our lives. We have spent the last week reviewing the virtues that will help us to cultivate a deeper understanding of ourselves and God—simplicity, humility, discernment, stillness, and prayer. Cultivating these attitudes will slowly help us clear away the external distractions and create space in our lives for talking with and listening to God. From this clearer viewpoint we are better positioned to see the small weeds of the passions as they begin to sprout up in our hearts and to tackle them before they come into full bloom and their roots become deep and entrenched.

As we discover on this forty-day pilgrimage, there are many things we can do with our time, but the simple act of spending time in prayer with the Lord is likely the most fruitful. The act of prayer is not just reciting words or asking God for comfort; it is time to *be* with God. It is time we spend opening ourselves to Him, recognizing the beauty in our lives—the gifts we already have that show us God's love—and giving thanks for all these things. Prayer also includes time spent sharing our failings and disappointments and asking for mercy and strength.

It is within this intangible relationship, this mystery of opening ourselves up to God and inviting Him into our souls, that we
make the space for Him in which we are transformed and our
passionate natures can be tamed. By being still, by humbling
ourselves before Him and acknowledging our passions, we make
room for God to fill our souls. As we will find out in Part IX,
what is soul filling is God Himself, and He is love.

➤ PRACTICE ◄

Weaving Prayer into Daily Life

We have already acknowledged how much our prayer life
changes in these early days with a baby. Our need for prayer
grows too, as we are not only responsible for ourselves but
also for bringing our children into a life of prayer. Our best
hope is to model prayer for them while helping ourselves to
grow at the same time.

There are many ways to bring prayer into a mother's day.
Ways we have found to pray during these early days include:

» Praying during routine baby tasks such as feeding, changing, and soothing baby

» Singing hymns, psalms, and prayers to baby

» Knitting, stitching, or crocheting (if we enjoy these activities) while saying the Jesus prayer

» Making the sign of the cross whenever we notice worry,
impatience, or other temptations crossing our mind

» Using moments when we wake in the night to pray[21]

---

21 In her book *The Jesus Prayer: The Ancient Desert Prayer that Tunes
the Heart to God* (Orleans, MA: Paraclete Press, 2009), Frederica

» Giving thanks to God for the blessings in each routine task—as we rise, make the bed, prepare meals, wash the dishes, clean and fold laundry—in all things we can give thanks to the Lord and ask for His mercy

» Setting an alarm to go off at the times of the Hours (the daytime ones) and reciting a small prayer or simply making the sign of the cross.

⌒

It is not enough to say prayers: we must become, be prayer, prayer incarnate. All of life, each act, every gesture, even the smile of the human face, must become a hymn of adoration, an offering, a prayer. One should offer not what one has but what one is.

—PAUL EVDOKIMOV[22]

⌒

For Mind & Body

CHECK-IN

To foster dispassion we must take time to cultivate internal space and awareness. We do this by developing our self-awareness in regard to all our needs: physical, mental, and spiritual. We can start again with a simple check-in. How are you doing? Are you taking care of your needs? Have you connected with any friends or family that you miss lately? What do you need right now? As

---

Mathewes-Green describes this lovely practice, which she began when her children were babies and continues until this day.

22 Fr. Mario Attard, "Becoming a Living Prayer," *Times of Malta*, April 30, 2021, https://timesofmalta.com/articles/view/becoming-a-living-prayer.709977.

you read this, take a moment to close your eyes and pray about anything weighing on your heart.

This is a period of enormous growth for our babies and for us. Perhaps some of the practices we've been trying have been uncovering uncomfortable emotions. Perhaps in our reflections and journaling we've noticed feelings that are difficult to handle on our own. This is to be expected. Growth is hard. Remember that struggles are here to teach us humility and help us not to fall into the trap of believing we can do it all on our own. Reach out and get help. Talk to your partner, a close friend, sibling, parent, or your priest. Sometimes we might hear "Oh, this is just new motherhood. You're fine!" While this may be true, it often isn't the reassurance we need; instead it can make us feel more alone and scared. If this happens, we must keep reaching out until we find someone who can listen properly. If you are really struggling and not finding help in your support system, this might be a good time to talk to a professional, such as your healthcare provider or a counselor.

PART IX

The Supreme Trinity among the Virtues

We are created in the image of God who is love, which means that love is our truest nature: love is our most authentic activity; love is our origin; and love is our destiny. We are fully who and what we were meant to be when we are loved and love in return.

—FATHER MARK O'KEEFE, BENEDICTINE MONK[1]

---

1   Quoted in *The Maternity of Mary*, p. 84.

DAY 37

Faith

We Are in God's Hands

[Faith] can make and create all things.

—SAINT JOHN CLIMACUS[2]

For we walk by faith, not by sight.

—2 CORINTHIANS 5:7

As a mother teaches her child to walk, so also God teaches us to have a living faith in Him. A mother will make the child stand, and leave it for a while by itself, then she will tell it to come to her. The child cries without its mother; it wants to go to her, but is afraid to attempt to move its feet; it tries to walk, makes a step, and falls down. God teaches the Christian faith in him in a like manner (faith being the spiritual way); our faith is as weak, as elementary as the child beginning to walk. The Lord leaves the man without His help and gives him up to

---

2   *Ladder*, p. 225.

*the Devil, or to various distresses and afflictions, and after-
wards, when he is in extreme need of help of being delivered
from them (for we are not ready to go to Him until we are in
need of salvation), He bids us to look on Him (we must absolutely look upon Him) and come to Him for that help.*

—ST. JOHN OF KRONSTADT[3]

*Now faith is the substance of things hoped for, the evidence of
things not seen.*

—HEBREWS 11:1

For the Soul

Many of us are familiar with Jesus' words about the mustard seed: "If you have faith as a mustard seed, you will say to this mountain, 'Move from here to there,' and it will move; and nothing will be impossible for you" (Matthew 17:20). Through the strength and promise of these words we understand the power of faith. Yet we may struggle to understand exactly what faith is.

For mothers, our faith plays out especially in trust in the Lord's providence and care for our little one(s). *We are in God's hands.* To really believe this in the core of our being, we must have faith; we must trust in God. This kind of trust is a true test of the depths of our faith. Imagine the agony of Abraham thinking he must sacrifice his beloved son. What faith he had in the Lord to walk toward such a task! Saint Mark the Ascetic describes how "God 'tested Abraham' (cf. Gen. 22:1–14), that is, God afflicted him for his own benefit, not in order to learn what kind of man Abraham was—for He knew him, since He knows all things before they

---

3   *My Life in Christ*, p. 44.

come into existence—but in order to provide him with opportunities for showing perfect faith."[4]

While we may or may not have trials like those of Abraham, each day brings its own challenges and situations that test our faith. How we respond to these events can sometimes unmask for us just how much we struggle to trust in God's grace.

Perhaps we struggle with trust generally. Perhaps we have had experiences that have shaken our trust. Maybe we simply find it hard to fully trust in someone we have never seen. Though there are many ways in which we know God, we do not see Him or know Him in the standard ways of the world. Our calculating mind must suspend disbelief and allow space for the heart to believe. We are strengthened by Jesus' words to Thomas after His Resurrection and appearance to His apostles: "Thomas, because you have seen Me, you have believed. Blessed *are* those who have not seen and *yet* have believed" (John 20:29).

We may also find that having a child has strengthened our faith. Maybe we are amazed at the mystery of our child and how she came to be in our arms. Having a child can help our faith to flourish as we recognize the glory of life that God has bestowed on each of us.

However strong our trust is in the Lord, this time away from church—and even our time later on in church with new responsibilities calling us away from full attention to the divine services—can be challenging. We may begin to feel that God is far from us or that we are far from God. Jesus' forty days at the beginning of His ministry were a time of temptation, and as such they also became a time of growth for Him. In his blog, *The Morning Offering*, Abbot Tryphon writes:

---

4   St. Mark the Ascetic, "No Righteousness by Works," no. 203, *The Philokalia*, vol. 1, p. 143.

Those periods of time when [God] seems distant, even per-haps a fictional being, are moments when He is actually closer to us than our own breath. These are the moments God is drawing us out of ourselves, and into communion with Him. . . . These moments strengthen us, and enable us to have a mature relationship with God, not unlike the mature rela-tionship the child develops with his parents, after taking those first steps, alone.[5]

While these early days may have been more challenging for some and smoother for others, we can recognize that this experience, like all of our experiences, offers opportunities for growth. In this new relationship with our child and all that it brings, God is, as Abbot Tryphon says, drawing us into communion with Him. As we re-enter the world after our time apart from church, let us place our trust in the Lord and pray for His mercy in strengthen-ing us. We can't know the future, but we can have faith that the Lord will be with us each step of the way and offer the strength we need.

SASHA

One of the hardest things for me in the postpartum times away from church was the lack of weekly connection with my faith community and other believers. Church, being with my parish family, is the one place I feel complete. I don't live close to my church, and during these forty-day periods, church felt very far away. Without the nourish-ment of weekly communion and surrounding myself with

---

5   Abbot Tryphon, "Where Is God?" *The Morning Offering* (blog), Ancient Faith Ministries, July 13, 2019, https://blogs.ancientfaith.com/morningof-fering/2019/07/where-is-god-3/.

people of faith, I truly found this time a time of wandering in the wilderness—of temptation and isolation—especially on a spiritual level.

In all honesty, I had a great time going out to Sunday brunch and getting out of the house a lot (especially with my second and third child, when staying home felt less tenable). But the most important part of my life—the one thing needful—felt painfully absent. I now see this was of my own making. God is never far from us, as Abbot Tryphon so beautifully reminds us. It is we who can drift in and out of communion and connection with Him. While the services are a vital way we stay connected, prayer, Scripture, spiritual reading, and connection with others can help remind us that we are never far from God. My faith must be lived out not Sunday to Sunday, but moment to moment in my personal relationship with God.

▷ PRACTICE ◁

Sharing Our Faith

We believe that God is "everywhere present and fills all things," but our daily actions may not always support this. One way to strengthen our faith is to focus on filling our lives with the things of God. The more we integrate our Faith into all aspects of our life and all our relationships, with those who share our Faith and with those who do not, the more we are able to remain faithful to our true selves at all times.

As mothers we are examples for our children. One way to teach our children and to keep ourselves alert and turned toward God is to get into the habit of making the sign of the cross frequently. Crossing ourselves is also a visual sign for others. "Neither do men light a candle, and put it under a bushel, but on a candlestick; and it giveth light unto all that are in the house. Let your light so shine before men, that they may see your good works, and glorify your Father which is in heaven" (Matt. 5:15–16 KJV).

We can also stay attuned by speaking of God as a natural outflow of our faith. Perhaps we add phrases into conversation that remind us of God in all things, such as "Glory to God," "May it be blessed," "God willing," or "I will keep you in my prayers." We can sign our correspondence to each other and any other believers in our life "with love in Christ." In whatever ways we are able, in love and humility, we must promote our Faith and always remember that Jesus has called us to be the "light of the world."

SARAH

As a child I always clued into our surroundings when my mom crossed herself. She did it often while driving—when we passed an accident, an ambulance, or a person on the street corner looking sad, hungry, or dangerous. She would cross herself when we were watching a movie and something tragic happened or someone swore. Her faith was a comfort to me, as was knowing she was watching out for everyone with a silent prayer in her heart. In this way, among others, she let her light shine and always reminded me that God is with us.

For Mind & Body

PHYSICAL STRESS RELIEF

As we come to our last few days together, we will leave you with some simple ways to soothe and care for your body. While there are many practices we have shared to help our mental and spiritual selves, the care and kindness we show our physical self is also important.

Take a few minutes for basic care of your skin, especially your hands and feet. Make yourself a cup of soothing herbal tea (raspberry leaf, which can increase uterine tone, and nettle leaf, which is full of vitamins and minerals and helps breastmilk production, are particularly good postpartum teas). Give yourself a few moments to practice relaxing your muscles and relieving tension with the exercise below. A guided recording of this and our other exercises can be found on our podcast, *A Sacred Beginning*, on ancientfaith.com.

> ➤ EXERCISE ◀

Progressive Relaxation

Progressive relaxation is an exercise we can use to relax when we feel wound up, to help us fall asleep, or to ease muscle tension. It is a simple practice that focuses on tensing and then fully releasing each of the muscle groups of the body in turn—beginning at the feet and working upward. Often our muscles are in a state of semicontraction, still ready for action from the stress and business of our days. The act of contracting the muscle can be helpful in allowing the muscle to then fully release.

Start sitting or lying down. Bring your attention to your toes and begin slowly and methodically to work your way up the body, tensing and then releasing each muscle group you can identify. At the end of the exercise, take a moment to notice how your body feels in this more fully relaxed state. Try to take any feelings of relaxation with you as you move forward into the next moment of your day.

DAY 38

Hope

All Things Are Possible

The power of love is in hope, because by it we await the reward of love.

—SAINT JOHN CLIMACUS[6]

While men walk in all the ways which there are in this world, they do not find peace, until they approach unto hope in God.

—ISAAC THE SYRIAN[7]

This hope is a foretaste of future blessings, of which the soul even now receives direct experience, and so it comes to know in part the surpassing richness of God's bounty, in accordance with the Psalmist's words, 'Taste and know that the Lord is bountiful' (Ps. 34:8). For He is the jubilation of the righteous,

6   *Ladder*, p. 228.
7   *Mystic Treatises by Isaac of Nineveh*, trans. A. J. Wensinck (Scotts Valley, CA: CreateSpace Independent Publishing Platform, 2012), p. 236.

*the joy of the upright, the gladness of the humble, and the
solace of those who grieve because of Him.*

—SAINT GREGORY PALAMAS[8]

For the Soul

In Matthew 19, the story of the rich young ruler, Jesus explains
both how difficult it is for a rich man to find salvation and
how even this can be achieved through God. His statement in
verse 26, "With men this is impossible, but with God all things
are possible," is the ultimate call for hope. In God, all things can
be. Many times we are faced with a problem and we can't see the
way forward or how the situation could ever be resolved without
calamity. After we have been blessed to come through it, we marvel at the wonders God has worked that we couldn't comprehend
or even imagine.

As the end of the first forty days with our new baby nears, we
will go forward into our new life, our "new normal" as a mother.
The days ahead will be filled with so much joy: gurgles and gig-
gles, babbling, grasping, rolling, crawling, walking, and running.
So much beauty and joy is ahead of us. We hope our offerings
have helped to lay a foundation for holding all this in love and
directing it up to God in thanksgiving.

We also know that there will be moments of pain, fear, crying, and worry. No parent is immune from the pangs of the heart
that a growing child brings: separation, illness or injury, and the
inability to be with and protect our child at all moments. We've
heard having growing children referred to as "my heart walking
around outside my body," and this captures the feeling exactly.

Yet through all of this, there is hope. When we place our hope

---

8   *The Philokalia*, vol. 4, p. 316.

in God, all things are possible. In our struggle, in our difficulty—in all things we hope in Him. It is the hope of raising the sick from their beds, of healing issues of blood and blindness. It is the hope of casting out demons, of obtaining and extending forgiveness, of babies born from barren wombs, of love in the face of hate, and of death trampling down death. When we feel our outlook is cloudy and our strength waning, we can hope in the power of our all-merciful God to help us through.

⌒

The heart itself is but a small vessel, yet there also are dragons and there are lions; there are poisonous beasts and all the treasures of evil. And there are rough and uneven roads; there are precipices. But there is also God, also the angels, the life and the kingdom, the light and the Apostles, the treasures of grace—there are all things.

—PSEUDO-MACARIUS[9]

⌒

➤ **PRACTICE** ◄

Joy

⌒

But let all those rejoice who put their trust in You;
Let them ever shout for joy, because You defend them;
Let those also who love Your name
Be joyful in You.

—PSALM 5:11

⌒

---

9   George A. Maloney, ed., *Pseudo-Macarius: The Fifty Spiritual Homilies and the Great Letter* (Mahwah, NJ: Paulist Press, 1992), p. 222.

We've shared our personal struggle in discussing our difficulties, our passions, and the trials of body and spirit we experienced as new mothers. In reflecting on hope, we must always remember that we are never lost. God is always with us and will not abandon us. It is our work never to abandon Him. "Be strong and of good courage, do not fear nor be afraid of them; for the LORD your God, He *is* the One who goes with you. He will not leave you nor forsake you" (Deut. 31:6). With God all things are possible.

Despite the challenges it poses, having a child can open up a wellspring of love and joy. This won't be the same for everyone—the timing and intensity will vary—but we want to recognize this love and joy as God's gift and His love bursting forth in a new way in our lives. As we come to the end of our time together, we want to help you recognize this in your own hearts and help you give yourself permission to let this joy flow. We say *permission* because we know from our own lives that it can be hard to let go of all the difficulties, worries, and tasks, and simply enjoy and marvel at the blessings in front of us. We also know that God calls us to do exactly this. We start by taking time each day to let this kernel of joy grow, to nurture it, and to pray that it will guide us through our days.

~

The Lord's mercies ... are new every morning.

—LAMENTATIONS 3:22–23

~

✠ PRAYER FOR A JOYFUL HEART ✠

Dear Lord, thank you for blessing me to be a mother. Forgive my lack of gratitude in moments of difficulty. I pray
that You will help me to be joyful in my days. I pray that the
deep well of love I have for my child may bubble up to the
surface and become visible to my child and those around
me. Please help me to be calm in the face of turmoil and
loving in the face of adversity. Please help me to be a joy and
light to those around me, leading them to You through the
darkness. Above all, please help me to be a beacon of Your
love for my family, drawing us ever closer to You. Amen.

For Mind & Body

THE MIND/BODY CONNECTION

In the field of dance/movement therapy, in which Sarah is a
board-certified therapist, the study of body posture and gesture
is an important tool for understanding a person's internal life. A
system of movement analysis and assessment is used to inform
treatment. Many of us instinctively understand this: if we see a
person with shoulders drawn forward and head down, we think
the person may be sad, lonely, or closed off to interaction. A
dance/movement therapist would note this as a "hollowing" posture. The therapist could then investigate how this plays out in
the person's relationships with the world and could help them
explore movements to create more integration.

The exercise below is one for all of us to do as we hope to let
love and joy flow in our hearts. We can make adjustments in our
body posture, making it more open and receptive, less inward-
facing and closed off. In the process, we can open our hearts and
become more receptive to love. Find a guided recording of this

and our other exercises on our podcast, *A Sacred Beginning*, on ancientfaith.com.

➤ EXERCISE ◄

Heart-Opener

Begin by sitting or standing with your hands on your lower belly. Just rest and breathe at a natural pace. After one minute, let your head fall gently to one side and then the other—feeling the stretch from the simple weight of the head tilting without force. Finally, let your head roll forward, bringing your chin toward your chest.

Begin the next step by lifting your shoulders toward your ears, then let them relax down as you imagine the top of your head reaching toward the ceiling. Repeat this two times and really notice the length of your neck when your shoulders are down and the top of your head lifts upward. On an inhale, gently draw your shoulder blades together and downward, opening your chest, and gaze up toward the ceiling. Exhaling, tuck your chin to your chest and round your shoulders forward as you press your spine back. Repeat this three times.

Now bring your arms into the movement. As you breathe in, draw your shoulder blades back and down while opening your arms wide. Keep your arms at shoulder level and feel a gentle stretch along the front of the chest. As you breathe out, reach your arms straight out in front of your body, palms pressed together, stretching forward while tucking your chin and rounding your back. Do this for as many rounds as you like. End by wrapping your arms around the front of your body, giving yourself a big hug!

DAY 39

Love

Our Origin and Destiny

And now, finally, after all we have said, there remain these three that bind and secure the union of all: faith, hope and love; and the greatest of these is love, for God Himself is so called.

—SAINT JOHN CLIMACUS[12]

Love alone is enough to make a miracle happen.

—MOTHER GAVRILIA[11]

The life of the heart is love, whilst malice and enmity against our brother are its death. The Lord keeps us on the earth in order that love for God and our neighbor may wholly

---

12   *Ladder*, p. 225.
11   *The Sayings of Mother Gavrilia.*

penetrate our heart. This is what He expects from us all. This
is, indeed, the purpose of the world's standing.

—SAINT JOHN OF KRONSTADT[12]

For the Soul

So we come to the last rung of St. John's ladder. Along the way he has shown us what to nurture in our souls and what passions to resist so that we may be close to God. All of this leads to his final rung: love. We see here that of all the virtues, love is the highest. To all the sin and struggle and temptation, love is the answer. When asked by the Pharisees what is the greatest commandment of all, Jesus unhesitatingly responds, "'You shall love the LORD your God with all your heart, with all your soul, and with all your mind.' This is *the* first and great commandment. And *the* second *is* like it: 'You shall love your neighbor as yourself.' On these two commandments hang all the Law and the Prophets" (Matt. 22:37–40). This seems so incredibly simple; and yet love can be one of the hardest things we try to practice.

As Christians, we are called to love God and to love others as ourselves. A great blessing of becoming a mother is that it teaches us what this love might look like. Our love for our children, in its ideal and perfect state, is caring for the other as much as, if not more than, ourselves. It is joy and compassion. It is mercy and willingness to sacrifice. It provides us a glimpse into the kind of love God as our eternal Father has for us. Love is not a limited commodity. By God's grace, loving our children does not diminish our ability to love others but rather increases it.

Some of us may struggle with love. Perhaps we have never felt fully loved. Many of us struggle to love ourselves in a full and

---

12   *My Life in Christ*, p. 249.

healthy way as children of God. Most of us do not truly comprehend and internalize the love God has for us. These struggles may cloud our ability to love our children with our whole heart. If we know this to be true, we must work to break down and resolve these barriers that keep us from truly realizing our human potential and that ultimately keep us from coming into full, loving communion with God. As St. John of Kronstadt reminds us, this is the primary task of our earthly lives.

⁓

What makes a person holy is love. . . . You won't become saints by hounding after evil. Ignore evil. Look towards Christ and He will save you.

—SAINT PORPHYRIOS[13]

⁓

To start, we must simply allow ourselves to love our baby. If this is hard for us, then we can pray for openness of heart. We can pray for courage so that we can look fear in the face and not let it hold us back. We can open ourselves to the possibility of loving freely and fully. We can pray that this mother love will fill our hearts and overflow to those around us—to our spouses, to our children, to our neighbors. In our prayers we can ask the Lord to fill us with love.

As St. John reveals, "God is Love."[14] When we let Him into our hearts and lives, we let love in. We are created in God's image, an image of love. Love is what we were created for. We receive and express love through worship and communion with our Creator. Love is our true essence. Motherhood brings our understanding

---

13   *Wounded by Love*, p. 135.
14   *Ladder*, p. 225.

and ability to love to a whole new level. Bringing a child into our lives opens our hearts and offers opportunities for endless uncon- ditional and selfless love. We can choose to open our hearts con- tinually, even when it is hard, even when we are tired, angry, or upset. No matter the situation, we always have the opportunity to choose love and through this bring ourselves closer to Christ.

We can take heart knowing that, in motherhood, God has bestowed on us this gift of love. He has given us our baby as a teacher in love. Not only may we love our children with a love that is probably deeper and fiercer than any we have experienced before, but our children, especially when little, love us with a pure and unquestioning love. This is a blessing and a mystery. If we are able to receive and internalize this gift, it can warm our hearts to the all-consuming love that God has for us.

SASHA

I mentioned previously my tendency toward anger—rooted, I have no doubt, in pride. These passionate outbursts of anger are extremely humbling. By God's grace, they repeat- edly remind me just how much in need of God's infinite mercy I am. It is amazing to me that my children's response to my anger is often to come to me with "Mommy, I love you" and an offer of a hug. This is true even when I turn my anger on them. They are able to recognize the suffering in my anger, which I was blind to, and to provide the soothing balm of love to help me through. This is an incredible gift!

~

A man who is wrathful with us is a sick man; we must apply a plaster to his heart—love; we must treat him kindly, speak to him gently, lovingly. And if there is not deeply-rooted malice

*against us within him, but only a temporary fit of anger, you
will see how his heart, or his malice, will melt away through
your kindness and love—how good will conquer evil. A
Christian must always be kind, gracious, and wise in order to
conquer evil by good.*

— ST. JOHN OF KRONSTADT[15]

⁓

For Mind & Body

LEARNING TO LOVE OURSELVES

A lovely older priest with whom Sasha once took confession
always starts the confession by asking the penitent to repeat, "I
don't love God enough. I don't love my neighbor enough. I love
myself too much." This is a beautiful and true sentiment about
love, and yet, as Sasha's personal reflection above speaks to, many
of us don't love ourselves *in the right way.*

We may be fiercely self-protective—wanting resources, physical comforts, and security. We may be self-righteous—unwilling
to listen to the opinions of others and desiring recognition. But
this is not truly loving ourselves. These desires are born from our
own sinfulness. The kind of firm, patient, and unconditional love
that God has for us, and asks us to have for our children, is often
lacking when we connect with ourselves. This inability to recognize our own need for and worthiness of love profoundly affects
our ability to recognize and receive the love of others, as well as
our ability to express our love for others. We are commanded
to love one another as we love ourselves. We are encouraged to
put others' needs before our own. Yet, as we have emphasized
throughout this book, as mothers we don't do ourselves or our

---

15   *My Life in Christ*, p. 117.

children any favors if we forget to recognize that we also have needs and that the greatest of these is for love.

Opening ourselves to the love of God and showing love toward ourselves can be difficult for many of us. Sometimes, in our struggle, what we need most is kindness and care. Through God's mercy, we can often provide this for ourselves. We have shared many ways to do this, such as speaking kindly to ourselves through positive self-talk, acknowledging that we are not perfect, repenting and moving forward from our failings, and being compassionate toward ourselves.

Having compassion for ourselves can allow us to grow and heal as we show ourselves love that is rooted in Divine Love. Through self-compassion and calling on the Lord, we can learn to soothe ourselves in the same way we would soothe our child, caring for ourselves in a way that imitates God's care for us. We see this compassion and care we can have for ourselves echoed in Scripture:

Blessed be the God and Father of our Lord Jesus Christ, the Father of mercies and God of all comfort, who comforts us in all our tribulation, that we may be able to comfort those who are in any trouble, with the comfort with which we ourselves are comforted by God. For as the sufferings of Christ abound in us, so our consolation also abounds through Christ. (2 Corinthians 1:3–5)

Let us take our consolation in the love of God. Let us hold ourselves accountable to His holy word and commandments, and when we struggle and fail, let us treat ourselves as our heavenly Father treats us—with compassion and love.

SARAH

I was blessed with a mother who knew how to love fully and always held the conviction that God loved us. As a mother myself, I realize that the unconditional love my mother has shown me over my lifetime, as ungrateful as I can be at times, is drawn from an infinite well—God's love. In my children's infancy, my love was pure and untested by daily trials. As my children grow, this love only deepens, grows more nuanced, developing layers of beauty, detail, and richness formed through weathering storms, trials, and joys, like the patina on a copper bell. There is strength in this love. Through my marriage and children, I am able to more fully understand 1 Corinthians 13, especially that love "bears all things, believes all things, hopes all things, endures all things."

This depth of love helps me to begin to comprehend God's true essence: Love, an infinite expanse that contains all things. Through the love of my husband and children, and in loving them in return, my compassion and love for myself can grow. This helps me reaffirm that God loves and forgives me as well. As I try to root myself in the love and mercy of God, I see His glory through love for my family.

➤ PRACTICE ◄

Resting in God's Love

Christian author and speaker Matthew Kelly shares how having a child helped him to understand more fully the all-encompassing love that God has for us.

But if I had any doubts about God's love for me they were quickly banished when my first child . . . was born. Those first weeks following his birth were an incredibly powerful spiritual time for me. I had this awe. I remember thinking over and over again, "If I can love my son this much and I am weak and broken, flawed and limited, imagine how much God loves us." My imperfect love provided profound insight into God's love.[16]

He goes on to relate a practice that he performed in those first weeks after becoming a father which he called "resting in God's love." Here we offer an adaptation of this practice.

If possible, practice this when you are able to sit quietly observing your sleeping child. No matter how frustrated we may be with ourselves and with our babies, a moment when they are sleeping often allows us to reconnect with how precious, tiny, vulnerable, and *ours* they really are.

Find a comfortable seat where you can rest your body. Perhaps tuck an extra pillow behind your back or under your legs. Put your feet up. Wrap a warm blanket around yourself if it is chilly. Get cozy and begin to simply gaze at your child.

You are just beginning to fall in love with this child. For some, love hits like a lightning bolt the first time we hold our children in our arms; for others it comes on more gradually. No matter where on the continuum you fall, the love you feel now for this child is just the beginning of the depths of love they will open up for you. God has given you a gift of love.

---

16   Matthew Kelly, *Rediscover the Saints* (North Palm Beach, FL: Blue Sparrow Books, 2019), pp. 17–18.

Try to connect with how love feels in your body—perhaps it is a warmth in the middle of your chest, or a tingling throughout your body. Feel how warming and nourishing this outflowing of love can be. Begin to imagine how God gazes on you as His child—precious, tiny, vulnerable, and *His*. Recognize the magnitude of the love you feel for your child and imagine that love infinitely enlarged by the completeness of God's love. Allow yourself whatever time you can to feel the radiation outward of your own imperfect love and the all-encompassing glow of God's perfect love. Abide in His love.

⁓

"As the Father loved Me, I also have loved you; abide in My love."

—JOHN 15:9

⁓

PART X

Rejoining the World

Every mother's path is different; every child is unique, requiring a parent to listen closely to what that child is trying to say. But Love, with a capital L, which is secret code for loving like the Theotokos did, sacrificially, wholeheartedly, that kind of love is what I reach for. New mamas are already embedded with all sorts of good instincts, especially if they are pursuing a holy life. Being a mama is a lifelong pursuit, and I am still learning. May the holy Theotokos pray for us.

—JANE G. MEYER[1]

---

1   Children's author and editor Jane G. Meyer, guest on Hannah Vasquez, "What They Wish They Knew," May 11, 2020 in *All These Things* podcast, https://www.ancientfaith.com/podcasts/allthesethings/what_they_wish_they_knew.

DAY 40

Churching

The Start of Illumination

Now when the days of her purification according to the law
of Moses were completed, they brought Him to Jerusalem to
present Him to the Lord.

—LUKE 2:22

Welcome to the end of forty days postpartum and the beginning of life in the Church with a new child! This transition marks the close of a sacred time of healing and early motherhood. We may still be healing, and many of us certainly will still feel very new at motherhood, but this traditional time of rest is ending, and we are moving into a fuller participation in life and church. God willing, our baby will soon be baptized and a full member of the Body of Christ.

Our modern-day churching ceremony is a sacred blessing for us and our child that honors and replicates the presentation of Jesus at the temple by the Theotokos, which we celebrate on the Feast of the Meeting of the Lord. Like Mary, we return to the church forty days after our child's birth. Prayers are offered first for the mother, then for the child, and then for the two together, to welcome mothers back into full sacramental life and to welcome the child into the fold of the community and the life of Christ.

Below, we offer a selection of the prayers known as the churching prayers. Take a moment to read them now, as the first moments back in church are full of busyness and emotion and, quite possibly, a loudly crying baby!

✛ PRAYERS FOR A WOMAN ✛
ON THE FORTIETH DAY OF CHILDBIRTH[2]

Then bending down his head to the mother, as she stands with the infant, the Priest makes the Sign of the Cross over them; and touching the infant's head, he says the Prayer:

O Lord God Almighty, Father of our Lord Jesus Christ, Who by Thy word has created all nature, both reason-endowed *men* and irrational *animals*, and hast brought all things from nothingness into being, we pray and entreat Thee: Thou hast saved this Thy servant, N., by Thy will. Purify her, therefore, from every sin and from every defilement, as she now draws near to Thy holy church; and let her be counted worthy to partake uncondemned, of Thy Holy Mysteries. . . .

And bless the child which has been born of her. Increase him (*her*); sanctify him (*her*); enlighten him (*her*); render him (*her*) chaste; and endow him (*her*) with good understanding. For Thou hast brought him (*her*) into being, and hast shown him (*her*) the physical light, and hast appointed

---

2   *Holy Needs*, pp. 10–15.

him (*her*) in due time to be counted worthy of spiritual light, and that he (*she*) may be numbered among Thy holy flock, through Thine Only-begotten Son with Whom Thou art blessed, together with Thy Most-holy, Good and Lifegiving Spirit, now and ever, and unto the ages of ages. Amen.

PRAYERS FOR THE MOTHER[3]

O Lord our God, Who didst come for the salvation of the human race, come also upon Thy servant, N., and count her worthy, through *the prayers of* Thine honorable Priest, of entrance into the temple of Thy glory. Wash away her bodily and spiritual uncleanness, in the completion of the forty days. Make her worthy also of the communion of Thy precious Body and Blood. For sanctified and glorified is Thy most-honorable and majestic Name, of the Father, and of the Son, and of the Holy Spirit, now and ever and unto the ages of ages. Amen.

PRAYERS FOR THE CHILD[4]

The Priest, making the Sign of the Cross over the child, prays:

---

3   As we noted with the birthing prayers, the language of impurity in the churching prayers has caused some women to feel ashamed and unsupported by the Church. In her book *Maternal Body*, Carrie Frederick Frost discusses the history of the churching prayers and how the earliest versions from the fifth century do not contain impurity language. She writes that this language came in around the twelfth century or later and suspects it was influenced by the ideas of the Christian West. Different jurisdictions use different prayers, and changes have been made in some jurisdictions to reflect this. We can hear the prayers for what they offer to us now, in understanding of the love and care our Church has offered us throughout history.

4   Some priests perform the entire churching when the mother and infant first return to church, separate from and prior to the baptism. Some priests perform the initial churching prayers at the entrance of the child into the church and the second portion as the post-baptismal procession for infants.

O Lord our God, Who on the fortieth day wast brought
as an infant into the Temple, according to the Law, by
Mary the Bride Unwedded and Thy holy Mother, and wast
borne in the arms of righteous Simeon. Do Thou Thyself,
O Omnipotent Master, bless this infant that has been presented, that he (*she*) may appear before Thee, the Creator of
All, and do Thou increase him (*her*) in every work that is
good and well-pleasing unto Thee, driving away from him
(*her*) every adverse power by the sign of the likeness of Thy
Cross, for Thou art He that preserveth infants, O Lord, that
being counted worthy of holy Baptism, he (*she*) may receive
the portion of the Elect of Thy Kingdom, being preserved
with us by the grace of the Holy, Consubstantial and Undi-
vided Trinity. For unto Thee are due all glory, thanksgiving and worship, together with Thy Father Who is without
beginning, and Thy Most-holy, Good and Lifegiving Spirit,
now and ever and unto the ages of ages. . . . Amen.

The ritual and prayers of churching are deeply important for
both mother and child. Just as in marriage, husband and wife are
united with one another as one body in the Church, so churching
unites mother, father (if he is present), child, Church, and God.
For mothers, the churching is our official re-entry into church life
after giving birth; it prepares us spiritually to return to liturgical life. In returning to church, we are welcomed back into our
community with our newest charge and are granted an extended
family that will join with us in raising our child in the knowledge
and love of God.

For our child, this is the first introduction to the church

We include here a selection of the prayers said pre-baptism, which do not
include the child being carried around the church and to the sanctuary.

temple. Our baby is shown where he will worship, sing, and commune. Through this service we hand our child over to God—both symbolically and literally, giving our child into the hands of the priest as God's representative. This is the start of our child's life in the Church, and we can see how our children truly are *in God's hands.*

We have come full circle from DAY 1: BIRTH. Let's return to Fr. Schmemann's book *Of Water and the Spirit,* where he writes about the connection of churching with the first Mother of the Church, the Theotokos. "The ultimate joy and meaning of this rite is to be found—as the Church understands and experiences—in the light and joy of the mystery of Mary."[5] As each mother is welcomed back into the Church with infant in arms, she is greeted by an icon of the Theotokos with Christ in.her arms. The Theotokos is our God-bearer, mother to us all, and the ultimate example of maternal love and guidance. As Fr. Schmemman writes, she is "full of grace. And now this grace fills the Church. And it is this grace—the grace of Mary, the grace of the Church—that each mother *receives* yet also *gives* as she brings her child to God."[6] Through her divine vocation Mary received the grace of God. In this moment when we come to church holding our child before the Theotokos and her Son, we also share in this grace.

Returning to church may feel to many of us like coming home. Having our child enter into the church is a sacred moment. With God's grace it will be the start of our child's whole lifetime in the Church. Congratulations! May God bless you and your family!

---

5   *Of Water and the Spirit*, p. 136.
6   Ibid., p. 146.

Epilogue

While the end of our forty days marks the end of our prescribed rest, as well as the end of our journey together, it is just the beginning of your next steps in motherhood and in the spiritual upbringing and celebration of this child. We are so grateful to have shared this time with you and to have shared some of our own joys and failings, our wisdom and ignorance. While life slowly returns to its own new normal, and our period of voluntary exile is ending, we remember that St. John's ladder begins with exile and that we are always invited to remind ourselves that "our citizenship is in heaven" (Phil. 3:20). As Paul writes in his Epistle to the Romans, "Do not be conformed to this world, but be transformed by the renewing of your mind, that you may prove what *is* that good and acceptable and perfect will of God" (Rom. 12:2).

We hope you have had the chance to become intentional in some areas of your life and to set some priorities that will help guide you in the weeks, months, and years ahead. We leave you with a prayer and a quick reference to our golden rules of motherhood to help you on your way. Just formulating these golden rules has brought comfort and direction to both of us in many challenging mothering moments.

✢ A MOTHER'S PRAYER ✢

Lord, thank You for my child and for this precious gift of time granted me to spend in communion and connection with my child. Thank You, Lord, also for trusting me to be this child's mother. I know that this child is a gift that will make me grow and struggle toward my own salvation. I know my child is a gift of love to teach me more fully to love You, others, and myself.

Loving my child and watching him/her grow and live in the world will test my faith in so many ways. Strengthen me for this journey. Bless me with words of grace for those around me and for myself. Help me to acquire the spirit of peace that St. Seraphim of Sarov believed will save not only my family but a thousand souls around me. Grant me patience and the knowledge that, to be the mother I need to be, I will need others' and Your loving guidance and support in abundance. Help me to understand the truth of Your words that Your "strength is made perfect in weakness," and grant me to rather "boast of my infirmities" that Your power might rest upon me (2 Cor. 12:9).

Forgive my many weaknesses and lack of faith in Your divine Providence. Heal my unbelief and grant me the grace to manage my dealings with others and myself with love and the firm faith that You are above all. Most of all, O Lord, bless my efforts to bring my child(ren) to You over and over again, until they abide in Your love and love You as I aspire to love You. For all this, grant me a spirit of continual prayer and turning to You. Help me to start today. In the name of the Father and the Son and the Holy Spirit. Amen.

Golden Rules of Motherhood

» Prayer Is the Way

» Use the Struggle to Grow in Faith and Love

» Our Peace Brings Peace

» We Are in God's Hands

» We Start Where We Are

Loss

Give rest, O Lord, to the souls of your servants who have departed this life.[7]

If you have lost a child due to miscarriage, stillbirth, or infant death, this section is for you. While we may have no immediate understanding of why this happened, we know that countless women have had to give up the bodies of their babies and turn over the souls of their children to the keeping of the Lord. While it may bring little comfort in this moment, we hold that we are children of God, and eventually we all hope to return to Him. As Christians, our understanding of this world and our purpose is to live our lives so that we may find ourselves once again with God. Our child is in the most perfect place, resting in the quiet harbor of the Lord.

Some women choose to take forty days to heal after the loss of a child. The Church offers prayers in your loss and time to rest, grieve, and begin to heal. Reach out to those who are most comforting and able to support you physically, emotionally, and spiritually. Jenny

---

7   Funeral refrain from the Panikhida service.

Schroedel has written a beautiful book called *Naming the Child,* which offers suggestions for processing the grief of pregnancy and infant loss. In her book *Fertile Ground*, Laura Jansson shares her own story of miscarriage, how she honored the life of her son, and his role in the spiritual life of her family.

∽

After my miscarriage, I found the forty days at home to be very healing. I was just not ready to deal with the outpouring of sympathy from folks at church yet; I would have just cried through the whole Liturgy. I needed that time to "get myself together" and process it. I knew they were praying for me, and that helped. I just needed the space and time to myself.

—SUSAN, ORTHODOX MOTHER

∽

In the weeks, months, and years to come, allow yourself to grieve. Give yourself space for grief. You will not be the same person you were before you became a mother who has lost a child. In your new identity you will discover what this means for you and how it will transform you. If you have lost a child prior to the birth of this new baby in your arms, you may have memories, grief, and fear that will surprise you in the midst of your joy. This is very normal. Be easy with yourself during this time and with respect to these feelings.

Rely on the love of the Lord to hold you through your darkest pain, and allow yourself to be transformed. Call out to the The-otokos—she was a mother who endured the torture of seeing her son on the Cross, and she knows the depth of pain a mother feels in losing her child. Ask her intercessions for the soul of your baby and for yourself to help you in your suffering.

SASHA

As a family doctor providing prenatal care and care for mothers and newborns, I have been witness to many miscarriages, both early and later in pregnancy. I have had patients who lost their child only hours after birth and patients who lost children into adulthood. The suffering of losing a child is one that cannot be put into words; the needs of a parent who has lost a child are unique and often private.

In my own life I have been through three miscarriages. I finished the manuscript of this book while five and a half months pregnant. Having had two miscarriages shortly before this pregnancy, and being older, so that the risks for problems are greater, I held the pregnancy at arm's length for a long time. I was unwilling to connect or fully acknowledge this life growing inside of me for fear of losing it.

During that time I began reading Laura Jansson's book *Fertile Ground* and found a section that helped me to recognize the gift of this life I was carrying and to remember that God's love for my unborn child was stronger than any love I could imagine. I realized that though there was always a chance this child might never end up in my arms or running around my home wreaking havoc, he was a blessing and he was my child. I could love him *and* release him later, if that was God's will, and still make it through. By God's grace, all went well, and my little boy is nestled in my arms now, during my forty days, as I review the final edits before this book goes to press.

The physician part of my brain that regularly counsels on the frequency of miscarriage has kept me from processing my own losses in a personal way. However, I do harbor some hopes that, if I am found worthy and reconciled into God's love in the final judgment, I will meet the souls of my three "lost" children who, in truth, fulfilled my biggest dream for any of my children—the hope of being held for eternity in the bosom of Abraham.

Postpartum Arnica Compress
to Ease Post-Birth Swelling

After you give birth, you will likely have a lot of swelling and discomfort. This arnica compress is helpful to use after going to the bathroom and to place on C-section stitches. Arnica is known to soothe and to ease swelling and bruising. You (or a loved one) can make a batch before you give birth and keep it in your freezer for when you get home. The remaining diluted arnica can be saved in a jar to add to sitz baths.

Ingredients

10 oz. boiled and cooled water
1 bottle of arnica essence (found at drugstore or online)
1 package of sterile gauze pads
1 roll of aluminum foil
Scissors

To Make

Dilute 1 oz. of arnica essence in 10 oz. water. Soak sterile gauze pads in mixture. Cut foil squares (the same number as gauze squares) but make the foil squares at least an inch bigger around, as you will be using them to contain the gauze. After the gauze has soaked, put each individual square in a square of foil and fold into a little packet. Put all the packets in a freezer bag and freeze.

To Use

Take a foil compress out of the freezer each time you go to the bathroom. Open the packet and let it sit at room temperature for 2–4 minutes. After using the toilet, pour mildly warm water over the sore area (often hospitals give you a spray bottle or cup to use for this purpose) and blot dry. Remove the compress from the foil (discard the foil) and put the compress on top of your postpartum pad. Leave in place for 30 minutes. The coolness will soothe the area, and the arnica helps to reduce swelling and pain.

Resources

Below is a list of some of our favorite resources. Our list is not exhaustive, and we are sure you will find many favorites of your own. Many of our favorite spiritual books were cited throughout the book as well.

Breastfeeding

www.kellymom.com

Breathing

Belisa Vranich, *Breathe* (New York: St. Martin's Press, 2016)

Gratitude

Ann Voss Kamp, *One Thousand Gifts* (Grand Rapids, MI: Zondervan, 2010)

Meal Train Resources

www.takethemameal.com

Parenting Resources

Philip Mamalakis, *Parenting Toward the Kingdom* (Chesterton, IN: Ancient Faith Publishing, 2016)

Laura Markham, *Peaceful Parents, Happy Kids* (New York: Penguin Group, 2012)

Kim John Payne, *Simplicity Parenting* (Ballantine Books, 2010)

Molly Sabourin, *Close to Home* (Ben Lomond, CA: Conciliar Press, 2008)

Prayer

Annalisa Boyd, *The Ascetic Lives of Mothers* (Chesterton, IN: Ancient Faith Publishing, 2014)

Elissa Bjeletich and Caleb Shoemaker, *Blueprints for the Little Church: Creating an Orthodox Home* (Chesterton, IN: Ancient Faith Publishing, 2016)

Holly Pierlot, *A Mother's Rule of Life* (Nashua, NH: Sophia Institute Press, 2004)

Perinatal Mood and Anxiety Disorders and Postpartum Depression

Postpartum Support International: www.postpartum.net

Postpartum Stress Center: www.psi.com

Pregnancy, Birth, and Postpartum

Laura Jansson, *Fertile Ground: A Pilgrimage through Pregnancy* (Chesterton, IN: Ancient Faith Publishing, 2019)

Ina May Gaskin, *Ina May's Guide to Childbirth* (New York: Bantam Dell, 2003)

Oscar Serrallach, *The Postnatal Depletion Cure* (New York: Hachette Book Group, 2018)

Postpartum Healing

Postnatal Rescue with Erin O'Brien (video). The video has three levels. It starts at the beginning and helps rebuild your back, pelvis, and core muscles to help you regain strength.

Sleep

www.amotherfarfromhome.com

Harvey Karp, *The Happiest Baby on the Block* (New York: Bantam Books, 2015)

Polly Moore, *The Natural Baby Sleep Solution: Use Your Child's Internal Sleep Rhythms for Better Nights and Naps* (New York: Workman Publishing Company, 2008)

Acknowledgments

SARAH

Thank you, Lord, for Your endless gifts and the opportunity to write this book. So many people supported me in creating this book, and I am so grateful. My spiritual father throughout my early life, Fr. Spyridon, and his beloved Matushka Xenia: you opened your home and family to me, and in the process showed me the true meaning of Christian love. From you I learned about the depth and beauty of Orthodoxy. To my confessor and priest, Fr. David, and his wife, Matushka Faith: together you are the strong and loving rock of our parish. The fruits of your labors are sweet and abound in the lives of your children and our parish. The examples of Matushka Xenia and Matushka Faith have both instilled in me the beauty of the Christian family and the saintly way of motherhood.

Thank you to my family, especially my aunts and uncles, who have supported and loved me, and to my younger brothers and sisters, who give me hope: I hope I can give you the same. To Jennifer and Carmen, thank you for your mothering. To my father, David, I am eternally grateful you searched for God and brought us to Orthodoxy. To my brother Daniel, I am so thankful for you in my life. To my Grandfather Russell, thank you for being a faithful believer and a constant and loving presence. To my Grandmother Nancy, who gave us shelter and cared for us with patience and love, I hold your words in my heart. For Suzanne, who took me under her wing and helped me to fly. To my father-in-law and mother-in-law, Cliff and Kathy, thank you for your love and for raising such a wonderful son.

I thank my mother, Katherine, for wrapping me in love and the security that God was above, even when life seemed to be falling apart. Your example and strength, your warm arms and faith, taught me about unending love and forgiveness and gave me hope in God. Your guidance in my own motherhood is invaluable to me—you are the best Omi.

So much of my life and faith is shared and worked out in conversation with my lifelong bosom friend and kindred spirit, Juliana. Thank you for your tireless ear and for talking through so many ideas and sharing your own. Your friendship is life-sustaining. I am so grateful for you.

This book would not have gotten off the ground without the team that made it possible for me to get the bulk of my writing started. Norma, Alicja, Elizabeth, Glenys, and Rebecca, I am so glad my children and home were in your care. Thank you to the little red library for providing a lovely space to write on Friday afternoons.

To my fellow mothers who have been with me throughout this journey, especially Christin, Mat. Juliana, Inna, Jess, Andrea, Monica, Alexis, the women of my parish, my neighbor Nickie, and my community of women friends: thank you for being my buoys when the water gets choppy.

To those of you who read our proposal and early drafts, Mat. Juliana, Jess, Andrea, Laura, and Hannah, thank you. Your help was invaluable. Laura, your telling me that we wouldn't be the last and we didn't have to be the best or write the definitive work freed me to relax and offer what I could offer.

To Lynnette, Melinda, Katherine, and all the Ancient Faith family, thank you for your help and for the chance to get our book into the hands of mothers. I pray that it will help each woman who reads it find comfort and strength and a deepening of faith and peace in the Lord.

Of course, this book would not be, or be what it is, without Sasha Rose Oxnard. Thank you for joining me in writing, for your patience and gentle guidance, and for being such a good cowriter and dear sister in Christ. It is rare and beautiful to have a friend to know and love over a lifetime. I am so grateful to have grown together with you. What a beautiful journey this has been for us!

And finally, to my husband: you are my proof of God's care and my rock through all of life's transitions, especially parent-hood. Thank you for believing in me and letting me rest in the safety of your love and our marriage.

SASHA

First and foremost to say that without Sarah Brangwynne, my partner in writing and in navigating the spiritual waters of moth-erhood, this book would never have come to be. I am an ideas person—I love big ideas. But the follow-through—the nitty-gritty of formatting, submission details and deadlines, red tape of any kind—often puts me off. Sarah's energy and enthusiasm buoyed me along the whole path, and her hard work and time commit-ment made it possible for me to add my voice to the rich and grow-ing voices of Christian and Orthodox women out there. I will be forever grateful to her for her perseverance, to-do lists, attention to detail, and loving-kindness in the face of many disagreements or differing points of view—not about the spiritual content but about the delivery and organization of the book. I also will be forever grateful for Sarah's friendship and for having her as a model of lovingly bringing our children to the Faith. Thank you also to her three daughters for giving of their mother's precious time and for being loving and God-filled companions for my own children. May the Lord grant them many years.

Thank you to my husband for many hours of taking the children so I could work on this book, for being my partner in all things in life and especially in the spiritual upbringing of our children, and for helping me always move forward in my own spiritual upbringing. I could never have imagined being blessed with someone who would embrace the Faith I grew up in with his heart and mind, and make it his own and our family's with such a genuine and loving example. Thank you to the priest who raised me in the Faith, Fr. Spyridon Schneider, who has been an earthly father to me as well as a spiritual one, and to his daughter Juliana, who is, and always will be, the closest thing I have to a sister of my own. Thank you finally to Ancient Faith Publishing for allowing us to share these words with an audience and also for all that they do to make each of us practicing the Faith in our own small ways know that we are part of something much bigger and a community of believers in communion and love.

Sarah Brangwynne is an Orthodox Christian and a wife, mother, and therapist who knows how wonderful and trying motherhood can be. Through the love of her family and relying on God, she takes it one day and one breath at a time. In addition to caring for her three children, who teach her every day, she enjoys finding the exquisite in small moments and capturing the glory of nature in her heart and through her camera lens. She is a licensed professional counselor and board-certified dance/movement therapist specializing in reproductive mental health. Sarah lives with her husband and children, along with their dog and five hens, in the Northeastern US. This is her first book.

Sasha Rose Oxnard is an Orthodox Christian and a mom. She also happens to be a family doctor practicing prenatal care and pediatrics, as well as a wife, friend, daughter, amateur gardener, blogger, and lover of music, dance, art, animals, nature, and all things playful. With this book she adds *writer* to the list. Sasha writes a blog for AFM on trying to raise children to love God and their Faith (*Shepherding Our Little Flock*). She has lived and worked in the US, UK, Brazil, and Mozambique. She currently lives, works, and prays in New England with her husband, four small children, a dog, two cats, and five chickens.

Ancient Faith Publishing hopes you have enjoyed and bene-fited from this book. The proceeds from the sales of our books only partially cover the costs of operating our nonprofit minis-try—which includes both the work of **Ancient Faith Publish-ing** and the work of **Ancient Faith Radio**. Your financial sup-port makes it possible to continue this ministry both in print and online. Donations are tax deductible and can be made at **www.ancientfaith.com**.

To view our other publications,
please visit our website: **store.ancientfaith.com**

 **ANCIENT FAITH RADIO**

Bringing you Orthodox Christian music, readings,
prayers, teaching, and podcasts 24 hours a day since 2004 at
www.ancientfaith.com